Ship Stability
Notes & Examples

Kemp & Young

Stanford Maritime Limited
Member Company of the George Philip Group
12–14 Long Acre London WC2E 9LP

First published 1959
Second edition (metric) 1971   Reprinted 1972, 1974, 1977
© 1971 P. Young

Printed in Great Britain at The Pitman Press, Bath

SBN 85309 042 4

Contents

	Useful Formulae	2
I	First Principles	3
II	Simpson's Rules	15
III	Ship Stresses	27
IV	Transverse Stability	41
V	Longitudinal Stability	68
VI	Drydocking	84
VII	Water Pressure	88
VIII	Free Surface	92
IX	Stability Data	97
X	Use of Imperial Units	115
	Examples for Exercise	124
	Index	128

STANFORD MARITIME LONDON

USEFUL FORMULAE

Page

R.D. $= \dfrac{\text{density of the substance}}{\text{density of fresh water}}$ — 4

Displacement $= V \times \delta$ — 7

TPC $= \dfrac{1.025A}{100}$ — 7

FWA in millimetres $= \dfrac{\text{\textcircled{S}}}{4T}$ — 8

Sinkage due to bilging $= \dfrac{\text{volume of lost buoyancy}}{\text{area of intact waterplane}}$ — 9

Morrish's formula:

C.B. below W/P $= \dfrac{1}{3}(\dfrac{d}{2} + \dfrac{V}{A})$ — 5

BM $= \dfrac{I}{V}$ — 41, 43

BM for a boxshape $= \dfrac{B^2}{12d}$ (transversely) — 43

BM for a triangular shape $= \dfrac{B^2}{6d}$ (transversely) — 43

Righting moment $= W \times GZ$ — 46

GZ $= GM \times \sin \theta$ — 46

New KG $= \dfrac{\text{Sum of the moments about the keel}}{\text{Sum of the weights}}$ — 54

GG_1 (when loading) $= \dfrac{w \times d}{W + w}$ — 57

GG_1 (when discharging) $= \dfrac{w \times d}{W - w}$ — 57

GG_1 (when shifting) $= \dfrac{w \times d}{W}$ — 58

$GG_1 = GM \tan \theta$ — 59

Simpson's Rules:

1st Rule   Area $= \frac{1}{3}h (y + 4y_1 + y_2)$ — 16

2nd Rule   Area $= \frac{3}{8}h (y + 3y_1 + 3y_2 + y_3)$ — 16

3rd Rule   Area $= \frac{1}{12}h (5y + 8y_1 - y_2)$ — 17

MCT 1 cm $= \dfrac{W \times GML}{100L}$ — 69

MCT 1 cm $= \dfrac{8T^2}{B}$ (approx. for a boxshape) — 70

Change of trim $= \dfrac{\text{Moments about C.F.}}{\text{MCT 1 cm}}$ — 70

Loss of GM when drydocking $= \dfrac{P \times KM}{W}$ or $\dfrac{P \times KG}{W - P}$ — 86

P (upthrust) $= \dfrac{\text{Trim} \times \text{MCT 1 cm}}{\text{Distance of sternpost from C.F.}}$ — 85

P (upthrust) $=$ Amount water has fallen in cm $\times$ T.P.C. — 85

Thrust due to water pressure $= A \times h \times \delta$ — 89

Loss of GM due to free surface $= \dfrac{i}{V} \times \dfrac{\delta t}{\delta s} \times \dfrac{1}{n^2}$ or $\dfrac{i}{W} \times \dfrac{\delta t}{n^2}$ — 93

Wall sided formula   GZ $= \sin \theta (GM + \frac{1}{2} BM \tan^2 \theta)$ — 49

CHAPTER ONE

First Principles

SI units bear many resemblances to ordinary metric units and a reader familiar with the latter will have no difficulty with the former. For the reader to whom both are unfamiliar the principal units which can occur in this subject are detailed below.

LENGTH

1 metre (m)	=	10 decimetres (dm)	=	1m
1 decimetre (dm)	=	10 centimetres (cm)	=	0.1m
1 centimetre (cm)	=	10 millimetres (mm)	=	0.01m
1 millimetre (mm)	=			0.001m

MASS

1000 grammes (g)	=	1 kilogramme (kg)
1000 kilogrammes (kg)	=	1 metric ton

FORCE

Force is the product of mass and acceleration

units of mass	=	kilogrammes (kg)
units of acceleration	=	metres per second squared (m/s^2)
units of force	=	kg m/s^2 or Newton (N) when acceleration is 9.81 m/s^2 (i.e. due to gravity). kg 9.81 m/s^2 may be written as kgf so 1 kgf = 9.81N.

WEIGHT is a force and is the product of mass and acceleration due to the earth's gravity and strictly speaking should be expressed in Newtons (N) or in mass-force units (kgf) however, through common usage the force (f) portion of the unit is usually dropped so that weight is expressed in the same units as mass.

1000kgf = 1 metric ton force = 1 tonne
so that 1 tonne is a measure of 1 metric ton weight.

MOMENT is the product of force and distance

$$\text{units of moment} = \text{Newton-metre (Nm)}$$

$$\text{as } 9.81 \text{ Newton} = 1 \text{ kgf}$$

$$9810 \text{ Newton} = 1000 \text{kgf} = 1 \text{ tonne}$$

Therefore moments of the larger weights may be conveniently expressed as tonnes-metres.

PRESSURE is thrust or force per unit area and is expressed as kilogramme-force units per square metre or per square centimetre (kgf/m^2 or kgf/cm^2). The larger pressures may be expressed as tonnes per square metre (t/m^2).

DENSITY is mass per unit volume usually expressed as kilogrammes per cubic metre (kg/m^3) or grammes per cubic centimetre (g/cm^3). The density of fresh water is 1 g/cm^3 or 1000 kg/m^3.

$$\text{Now 1 metric ton} = 1000 \text{kg} = 1\,000\,000 \text{g}$$

$$\text{which will occupy} \quad 1\,000\,000 \text{cm}^3$$

$$\text{but } 1\,000\,000 \text{ cm}^3 = 100 \text{cm} \times 100 \text{cm} \times 100 \text{cm}$$

$$= 1 \text{m}^3$$

so 1 metric ton of fresh water occupies 1 cubic metre. Thus numerically, $t/m^3 = g/cm^3$.

RELATIVE DENSITY was formerly, and is still sometimes referred to as, specific gravity. It is the density of the substance compared with the density of fresh water.

$$\text{R.D.} = \frac{\text{Density of the substance}}{\text{Density of fresh water}}$$

As density of fresh water is unity ($1t/m^3$), the relative density of a substance is numerically equal to its density when SI units are used.

ARCHIMEDES stated that every floating body displaces its own weight of the liquid in which it floats.

It is also a fact that when a body is placed in a liquid the immersed portion of the body will displace its own volume of the liquid. If the body displaces its own weight of the liquid before it displaces its own total volume then it will float in that liquid, otherwise it will sink.

Saltwater has a relative density of 1.025 thus 1.025 metric tons of salt water occupy 1 cubic metre or 1 metric ton of salt water occupies 0.975697569 cubic metres.

Iron has a relative density of 7.8 thus 7.8 tonnes of iron occupy 1 cubic metre or 1 tonne of iron occupies 0.0128205 cubic metres.

If one cubic metre of iron is immersed in fresh water it will displace one cubic metre of the water which weighs 1 tonne. As 1 cubic metre of iron weighs 7.8 tonnes it is clearly not displacing its own weight. Now consider the same weight of iron with an enlarged volume, say 2 cubic metres (an air space of 1 cubic metre having been introduced in the centre of the iron). If this enlarged volume is immersed in fresh water 2 cubic metres are displaced and these 2 cubic metres weigh 2 tonnes. There is still insufficient weight of fresh water being displaced for the iron to float so the volume of the iron will have to be further increased - without increase in weight - if the iron is to float. When the volume of the iron (and air space) reaches $7.8m^3$, $7.8m^3$ of fresh water will be displaced and this weighs 7.8 tonnes which is exactly equal to the weight of the piece of iron. The iron will now just float. If the volume of the iron is increased still further it will float with a certain amount of freeboard as, if the volume were to be completely immersed a weight of fresh water more than the weight of the iron would have been displaced.

We can now summarise by saying that if the R.D. of the body taken as a whole is less than the R.D. of the liquid in which it is placed then it will float in that liquid.

RESERVE BUOYANCY is virtually the watertight volume above the waterline. It is necessary to have a certain reserve of buoyancy as, when in a seaway with the ends or the middle unsupported, the vessel will sink down to displace the same volume as she does when in smooth water. This could result in the vessel being overwhelmed. This is illustrated below.

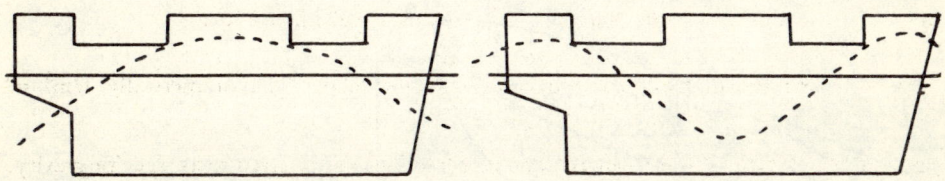

CENTRE OF BUOYANCY (B) is the geometrical centre of the underwater volume and the point through which the total force due to buoyancy may be considered to act vertically upwards.

In a boxshape   B is 0.5 d   )
In a triangular shape   B is 2/3 d   )   above the keel
In a shipshape   B is approximately 0.55 d   )

The position of the centre of buoyancy may be calculated by Simpson's Rules as shown on page 24. The approximate position may also be found by MORRISH'S FORMULA as under.

$$\text{C of B below waterplane} = \frac{1}{3}\left(\frac{d}{2} + \frac{V}{A}\right)$$

d is the draught
V is the volume of displacement
A is the area of the waterplane.

CENTRE OF GRAVITY (G) is that point in a body through which the total weight of the body may be considered to be acting. (It will be useful to remember that the resultant moment about the C of G is zero).

The methods of finding and calculating the position of G are given on page 13 and in Chapter IV.

WATERPLANE COEFFICIENT (Cw) is the ratio between the waterplane area (A) and the area of the circumscribing rectangle.

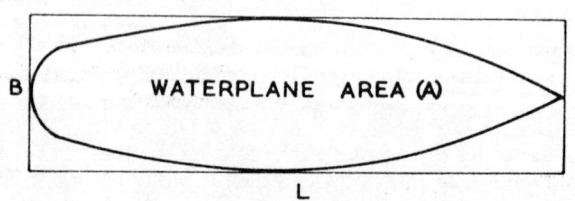

$$Cw = \frac{A}{L \times B}$$

L is the length of the waterplane
B is the breadth of the waterplane.

BLOCK COEFFICIENT OR THE COEFFICIENT OF FINENESS (Cb) is the ratio between the underwater volume (V) and the volume of the circumscribing block.

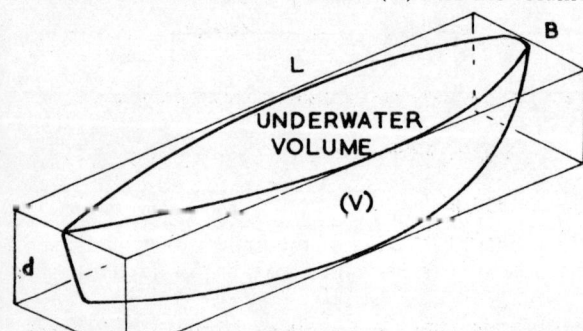

$$Cb = \frac{V}{L \times B \times d}$$

L is the length of the waterplane.
B is the breadth of the waterplane.
d is the draught.

PRISMATIC COEFFICIENT (Cp) is the ratio between the underwater volume (V) and the volume obtained from the product of the length between perpendiculars (LBP) and the underwater area of the midship section (Am). The coefficient gives an indication of a vessel's shape at the ends.

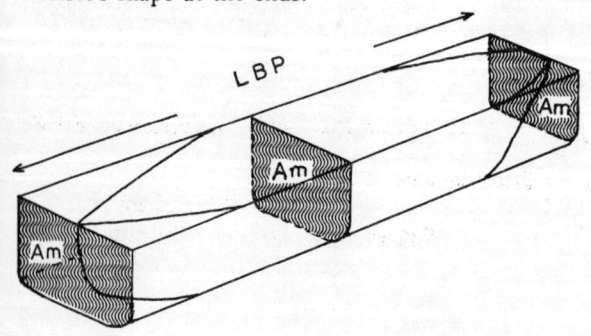

$$Cp = \frac{V}{LBP \times Am}$$

DISPLACEMENT

Volume of displacement in cubic metres   = $L \times B \times d \times C_b$

where L   =   length in metres
B   =   breadth in metres
d   =   draught in metres
C_b =   block coefficient (coefficient of fineness)

Displacement in tonnes   =   volume displaced x density
where above density is expressed in tonnes/m^3.

WORKED EXAMPLE 1

A vessel of triangular form length 100m, beam 12m, depth 6m is displacing 3030 tonnes in water relative density 1.010. What is her reserve buoyancy?

Volume of Displacement   = $\dfrac{3030}{1.010}$ =   3000m^3

Total volume of vessel   = $\dfrac{100 \times 12 \times 6}{2}$ =   3600m^3

Reserve Buoyancy   =   Total volume - volume of displacement

   =   3600 - 3000

   =   600m^3

TONNES PER CENTIMETRE IMMERSION (TPC) is the additional tonnage displaced when the mean draught is increased by one centimetre.

Additional volume displaced when the draught is increased by 1 centimetre is A x $\dfrac{1}{100}$ cubic metres where A is in square metres (m^2).

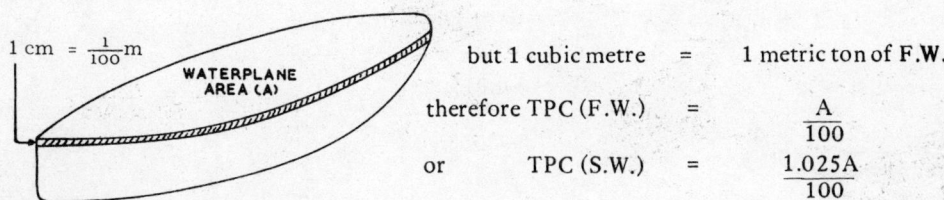

1 cm = $\frac{1}{100}$m   WATERPLANE AREA (A)

but 1 cubic metre   =   1 metric ton of **F.W.**

therefore TPC (F.W.)   = $\dfrac{A}{100}$

or   TPC (S.W.)   = $\dfrac{1.025A}{100}$

TO FIND THE FRESH WATER ALLOWANCE (FWA)

L, B, d in metres   A is waterplane area in m^2 T is TPC

$\triangle_F$ F.W. displacement at summer draught

$\triangle_S$ S.W. displacement at summer draught

Then L x B x d x Cb x density   =   displacement in metric tons

$$\triangle_F \quad x \quad 1.025 \quad = \quad \triangle_F \quad + \quad A \ x \ FWA \ \text{(in metres)}$$

$$\triangle_F \quad x \quad 0.025 \quad = \quad A \quad x \quad FWA \ \text{metres}$$

$$A \quad x \quad FWA \ \text{metres} \quad = \quad \frac{\triangle_F}{40}$$

$$\frac{100T}{1.025} \quad x \quad FWA \ \text{metres} \quad = \quad \frac{\triangle_F}{40}$$

$$FWA \ \text{metres} \quad = \quad \frac{1.025\triangle_F}{4000T}$$

$$FWA \ \text{millimetres} \quad = \quad \frac{\triangle_S \ x \ 1000}{4000T} \quad = \quad \frac{\triangle_S}{4T}$$

N.B. The FWA is given in this form in the Load Line Rules.

WORKED EXAMPLE 2

A vessel loads to her summer loadline at an up river port where the relative density of the water is 1.002. She then proceeds down river to a port at the river mouth where the water has relative density of 1.017, consuming 25 tonnes of fuel and water on passage. On loading a further 100 tonnes of cargo, it is noted that she is again at her summer loadline. What is her summer displacement in salt water?

Displacement tonnes   =   V x density

as she is always at the same draught V is constant..

so   V 1.002   =   displacement up river

V 1.017   =   displacement down river

and   V 1.017   =   V 1.002 + 75

$$V \quad = \quad \frac{75}{0.015}$$

V   =   5000m^3

so in salt water

Displacement   =   5000 x 1.025

=   5125 tonnes

We have shown how a steel ship can be made to float. Suppose we now pierce the vessel's hull in way of a midship compartment, as shown below;

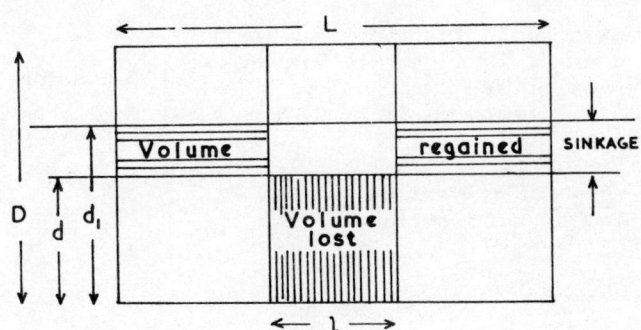

A volume of buoyancy l x B x d is lost. The vessel will sink lower in the water until this has been replaced, and part of her reserve buoyancy will be used. The total reserve buoyancy is (L - l) x B x (D - d), the portion which will be used is (L - l) x B x (d_1 - d).

i.e.   l x B x d   =   (L - l) x B x (d_1 - d)

so d_1 - d   = $\dfrac{l \times B \times d}{(L - l) \times B}$

or

$$\dfrac{\text{The increase in draught}}{\text{due to bilging}} = \dfrac{\text{The volume of lost buoyancy}}{\text{The area of the intact waterplane.}}$$

It can be seen that a reduction in lost buoyancy means less sinkage in the event of a compartment being bilged. The volume of lost buoyancy can be reduced either by fitting a watertight flat or by putting cargo in the compartment.

If the watertight flat is either at or below the waterline the length of the intact waterplane will be the full length of the vessel.

When cargo is in a compartment only part of the volume of the compartment will be available for water. The cargo will also contribute to the waterplane area.

PERMEABILITY is the relationship between the volume of a compartment and the volume available for water should the compartment be bilged. It is usually expressed as a percentage.

WORKED EXAMPLE 3

A box shaped vessel length 72m, breadth 8m, depth 6m, floating at a draught of 4m has a midship compartment 12m long. What will be the sinkage if this compartment is bilged if:-

a)   A watertight flat is fitted 5m above the keel?
b)   A watertight flat is fitted 4m above the keel?
c)   A watertight flat is fitted 2m above the keel?
d)   A watertight flat is fitted 4.5m above the keel?

a) $\text{Sinkage} = \dfrac{\text{Volume of lost buoyancy}}{\text{Area of intact waterplane}}$

$$= \frac{12 \times 8 \times 4}{(72 - 12) \times 8} = 0.8\text{m}$$

b) $\text{Sinkage} = \dfrac{\text{Volume of lost buoyancy}}{\text{Area of the intact waterplane}}$

$$= \frac{12 \times 8 \times 4}{72 \times 8} = 0.667\text{m}$$

c) $\text{Sinkage} = \dfrac{\text{Volume of lost buoyancy}}{\text{Area of the intact waterplane}}$

$$= \frac{12 \times 8 \times 2}{72 \times 8} = 0.333\text{m}$$

This assumes that the hull is bilged below the flat.

d)			
	The volume of lost buoyancy	=	$12 \times 8 \times 4$ = 384m^3
	Intact volume between 4m and 4.5m	=	$(72 - 12) \times 8 \times 0.5$
		=	240m^3
	Volume still to be replaced	=	$384\text{m}^3 - 240\text{m}^3 = 144\text{m}^3$
	Further sinkage	=	$\dfrac{\text{Volume still to be replaced}}{\text{Area of the waterplane (above W/T flat)}}$
		=	$\dfrac{144}{72 \times 8}$ = 0.25m
	Total sinkage	=	$0.5 + 0.25$
		=	0.75m

WORKED EXAMPLE 4

A vessel whose TPC is 12.3 is drawing 4m. A rectangular midship compartment 12m long 10m breadth and 6m depth has a permeability of 20%. What would be the mean draught if this compartment was bilged?

Vessel's waterplane area	=	$\dfrac{12.3 \times 100}{1.025}$	=	1200m^2
Area of compartment	=	12m x 10m	=	120m^2
Fully intact area			=	1080m^2
80% of compartment area			=	96m^2
Effective intact area				1176m^2

$$\text{Sinkage} = \frac{\text{Volume of lost buoyancy}}{\text{Area of the intact waterplane}}$$

$$= \frac{12 \times 10 \times 4 \times 20}{1176 \times 100} = 0.082\text{m}$$

Sinkage	=	0.082m
Old draught	=	4.000m
New draught	=	4.082m

It should be noted that if a bilged compartment is full and has no permeability, then, there will be no change of draught. An example of this is a double bottom tank filled with water ballast.

The effect on draught when an end compartment is bilged is discussed on page 81.

PRINCIPLES OF TAKING MOMENTS

A moment of a force (weight) about a point can be defined as being the product of the force and the perpendicular distance of the point of application of the force from the point about which moments are being taken. It is expressed in force-distance units which for problems associated with ships will be tonnes-metres.

A simple application of the principle of moments is that of calculating the position of the centre of gravity of a number of weights as shown below.

Consider a weightless bar AB, balanced at point F.

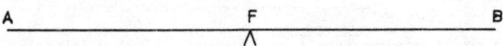

Place a weight of 5 tonnes 8 metres from F. This causes a moment of 5 x 8 tonnes-metres about F and consequently a rotation of the bar in a clockwise direction.

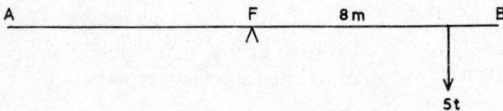

To keep the bar balanced, a similar weight of 5 tonnes may be placed at the same distance from F, but on the opposite side. The moments will now be equal and the rotational effect of the first weight counteracted.

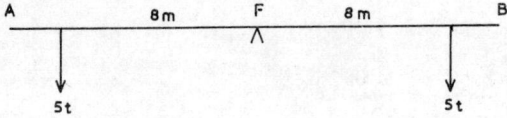

If however, there is only a weight of 8 tonnes available, we could place this at a distance of 5 metres to cause a moment which will again balance the original upsetting moment.

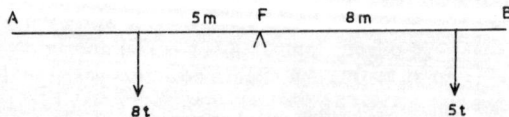

Weights of 6 tonnes and 11 tonnes at distances of 3 and 2 metres will give the same total moment on the left hand side of F. There are many combinations of weight and distance which can cause a moment of 40 tonnes-metres and so keep the bar balanced.

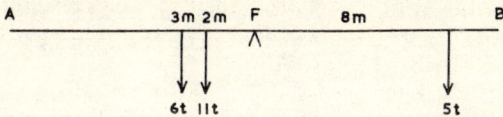

It must be clearly understood that the moment which is caused is all important, this is the product of weight and distance.

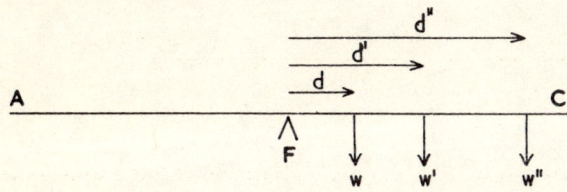

The bar AC, which is still weightless, now has weights w, w′, and w″ attached at distances d, d′, and d″ from F. To balance the bar we could put similar weights at similar distances on the opposite side of F, or we could put weight W, which is equal to the sum of w, w′, w″, at a distance D from F.

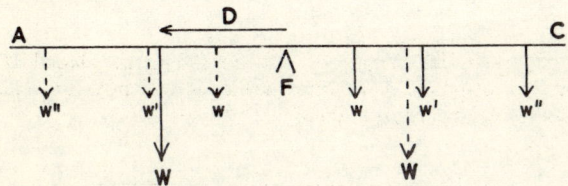

As W is replacing w, w′, w″, the position at which it is placed will be the centre of gravity of the weights w, w′, w″.

In order to find the distance D the moments each side of F should be equated i.e.

$$W \times D = (w \times d) + (w' \times d') + (w'' \times d'')$$

$$\text{then} \quad D = \frac{(w \times d) + (w' \times d') + (w'' \times d'')}{W}$$

In general terms

The distance of the centre of gravity of a number of weights from the point about which moments are taken $=$ $\dfrac{\text{Sum of the moments about the point}}{\text{Sum of the weights}}$

It should be understood that moments may be taken about any convenient point. When taking moments aboard ship, it is usual to take them either about the keel or centre of gravity for vertical positions of G, and either about the centre line or centre of gravity for transverse positions of G, examples of these are given on pages 54 and 57.

The same principles as those outlined above are used for calculating centres of areas or volumes (see pages 19 and 25), bending moments (see page 28) and trimming moments (see page 70).

CHAPTER TWO

Simpson's Rules

An essential in many of the calculations associated with stability is a knowledge of the waterplane area.

There are several ways by which this can be found, two of them being the TRAPEZOIDAL RULE and SIMPSON'S RULES. The former rule assumes the bounding curve to be a series of straight lines and the waterplane to be divided into a number of trapezoids (a trapezoid is a quadrilateral with one pair of opposite sides parallel), whereas the latter rules assume the curves bounding the area to be parabolic.

As the waterplane is symmetrical about the centre line, it is convenient to consider only half the area

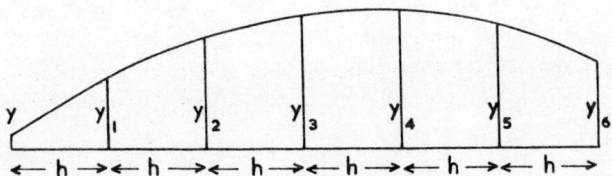

The figure above shows a half waterplane area with semi-ordinates (y, y_1, y_2, etc.) so spaced that they are equidistant from one another. This distance is known as the common interval (h).

By the trapezoidal rule the area $= h \times \left(\dfrac{y + y_6}{2} + y_1 + y_2 + y_3 + y_4 + y_5 \right)$

In general terms, the area can be expressed as :-

$$\left(\frac{\text{sum of the end ordinates}}{2} + \text{sum of the remaining ordinates} \right) \times \text{common interval}$$

It will be noted that the accuracy increases with the number of trapezoids which are formed, that is to say the smaller the common interval the less the error. Where the shape changes rapidly (e.g. at the ends) the common interval may be halved or quartered. The trapezoidal rule is used mainly in the U.S.A. In British shipyards Simpson's Rules, of which there are three, are in common use.

As examination syllabuses specifically mention Simpson's Rules the student is advised to study them carefully and to use them in preference to the trapezoidal rule.

SIMPSON'S 1st. RULE

This is to be used when the number of intervals is divisible by 2. The multipliers are 1 4 1, which become 1 4 2 4 2. . . . 4 1 when there are more than 2 intervals. This is shown below.

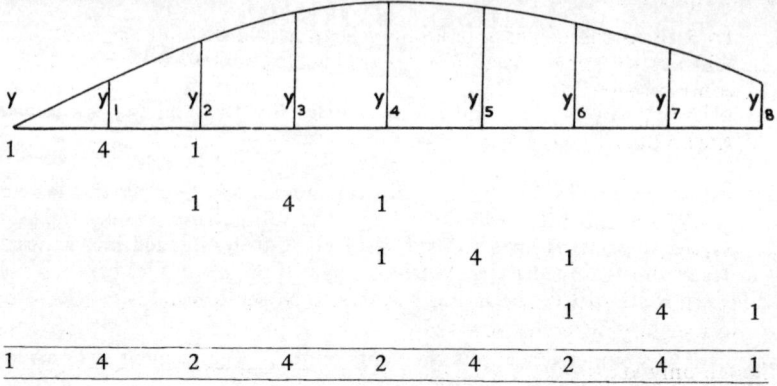

TO USE.

Multiply each of the ordinates by the appropriate multiplier; this gives a product (or function) for area. Add up these products and multiply their sum by $\frac{1}{3}$ of the common interval in order to obtain the area.

i.e. Area = $\frac{1}{3}$ h x $\left(y + 4y_1 + 2y_2 + 4y_3 + 2y_4 + 4y_5 + 2y_6 + 4y_7 + y_8 \right)$

SIMPSON'S 2nd. RULE

This is to be used when the number of intervals is divisible by 3. The multipliers are 1 3 3 1, which become 1 3 3 2 3 3 2 . . . . 3 3 1 when there are more than 3 intervals. This is shown below.

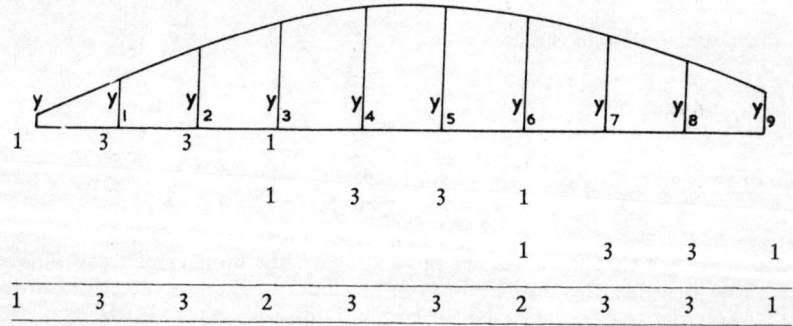

TO USE.

Multiply each of the ordinates by the appropriate multiplier to give a product for area. Add up these products and multiply their sum by 3/8 of the common interval in order to obtain the area.

i.e. Area = 3/8 h x $\left(y + 3y_1 + 3y_2 + 2y_3 + 3y_4 + 3y_5 + 2y_6 + 3y_7 + 3y_8 + y_9 \right)$

SIMPSON'S 3rd. RULE commonly known as the 5 - 8 rule.

This is to be used when the area between any two adjacent ordinates is required, three consecutive ordinates being given.
The multipliers are 5, 8, -1.

TO USE   To 5 times the ordinate bounding the area add 8 times the middle ordinate, subtract the other given ordinate and multiply this result by 1/12th. of the common interval.

Area ABCD $= 1/12\, h \times \left(5y + 8y_1 - y_2\right)$

Area CDEF $= 1/12\, h \times \left(5y_2 + 8y_1 - y\right)$

It will be noted that if we add the above areas together we have the 1st. rule in a slightly different form.

Although only areas have been mentioned above, Simpson's Rules are also used for calculating volumes. To do so a series of given areas is put through the rules; worked examples covering this are to be found further on.

Occasionally it will be found that either the first or the second rule can be used; in such cases it is usual to use the first rule.

When neither rule will fit the case a combination of rules will have to be used.

WORKED EXAMPLE 5

A waterplane has the following semi-ordinates spaced 45 metres apart:-
0, 9.0, 18.1, 23.6, 25.9, 26.2, 22.5, 15.7 and 7.2 metres respectively. Calculate the TPC.

No. of ordinate	½ ordinate	x	S.M.	= Product for area
1	0		1	0
2	9.0		4	36.0
3	18.1		2	36.2
4	23.6		4	94.4
5	25.9		2	51.8
6	26.2		4	104.8
7	22.5		2	45.0
8	15.7		4	62.8
9	7.2		1	7.2

Sum of the products   438.2

$\frac{1}{3} h = \frac{(45)}{3}$ x 15

½ Waterplane area $6573 m^2$

Waterplane area $13146 m^2$

$TPC = \dfrac{A}{100} \times 1.025 = \dfrac{13146 \times 1.025}{100}$

$= 134.75$

WORKED EXAMPLE 6

Using the semi-ordinates given in the previous example. Calculate the W/P area between the 3rd and 4th ordinates.

No. of ordinate	½ ordinate	x	S.M.	=	Product for area
3	18.1		5		90.5
4	23.6		8		188.8
5	25.9		- 1		- 25.9

Sum of the products   253.4

$$\frac{1}{12} h \ = \ \frac{(45)}{(12)} \quad x \quad 3.75$$

½ area   950.25m^2

area   1900.5m^2

Alternatively

No. of ordinate	½ ordinate	x	S.M.	=	Product for area
4	23.6		5		118.0
3	18.1		8		144.8
2	9.0		- 1		- 9.0

Sum of the products   253.8

$$\frac{1}{12} h \ = \ \frac{(45)}{(12)} \quad x \quad 3.75$$

½ area   951.75m^2

area   1903.5m^2

The slight discrepancy in the results is attributable to the different shape of the curve between the 2nd and 3rd and 4th and 5th ordinates.

WORKED EXAMPLE 7

A waterplane of length 270m and breadth 35.5m has the following equally spaced breadths:- 0.3, 13.5, 27.0, 34.2, 35.5, 35.5, 35.5, 32.0, 23.1 and 7.4 metres respectively. Calculate the waterplane coefficient.

No of ordinate	Ordinate	x	S.M.	=	Product for area
1	0.3		1		0.3
2	13.5		3		40.5
3	27.0		3		81.0
4	34.2		2		68.4
5	35.5		3		106.5
6	35.5		3		106.5
7	35.5		2		71.0
8	32.0		3		96.0
9	23.1		3		69.3
10	7.4		1		7.4

Sum of the products   646.9

$$\frac{3}{8}h = \left(\frac{270}{9} \times \frac{3}{8}\right) \quad x \quad 11.25$$

Waterplane area 7277.625m^2

$$\text{Waterplane Coefficient} = \frac{\text{Waterplane area}}{L \times B} = \frac{7277.625}{270 \times 35.5}$$

$$= 0.759$$

The geometrical centre of an area may be found by a method analogous to that used for finding the C.G. of a system of weights.

The "products for area" are multiplied by their distances from a convenient point (which is usually at either one end or the middle ordinate) or a special rule is used (see page 21) if the C.G. of an area between two ordinates is required. The sum of the "products for moment" so obtained is divided by the sum of the "products for area" to give the distance of the geometrical centre from the chosen point.

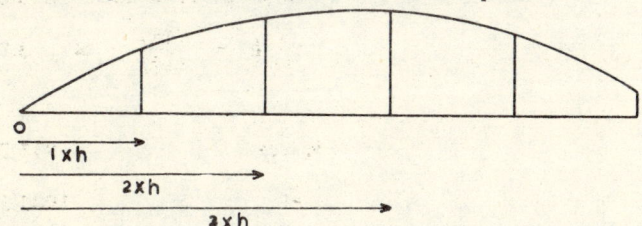

In the diagram above it is assumed that moments are being taken about the end ordinate. The 'product for area" for this ordinate is thus multiplied by (0 x h) to get the "product for moment". The distances for the succeeding "products for area" will be (1 x h), (2 x h), (3 x h) and so on. It will be seen that 'h' is a common factor and in order to make the arithmetic easier we may divide all our distances by it, thus making levers of 0, 1, 2, 3, and so on. The "products for moment" will now be 'h' times too small so we have to multiply this by 'h'. An example is shown overleaf.

WORKED EXAMPLE 8
    The half ordinates of a vessel's waterplane starting from forward and spaced 36 metres apart are:- 1.3, 11.2, 16.3, 17.5, 14.4, 8.7 and 3.0 metres respectively. Calculate the position of its geometrical centre.

1.   Using the 1st Rule and taking moments about fore end.

No. of ordinate	½ ordinate	x : S.M.	= Product for area	x lever	=Product for moment
1	1.3	1	1.3	0	0
2	11.2	4	44.8	1	44.8
3	16.3	2	32.6	2	65.2
4	17.5	4	70.0	3	210.0
5	14.4	2	28.8	4	115.2
6	8.7	4	34.8	5	174.0
7	3.0	1	3.0	6	18.0

Sum of the products   215.3 Sum of the products   627.2
        for area   for moment

Distance of geometrical centre from forward   = $\dfrac{\text{Sum of the products for moment} \times h}{\text{Sum of the products for area}}$

$$= \frac{627.2 \times 36}{215.3} = 104.873 \text{ metres}$$

2.   Using the 2nd Rule and taking moments about the after end

No. of ordinate	½ ordinate	x S.M.	= Product for area	x lever	= Product for moment
1	1.3	1	1.3	6	7.8
2	11.2	3	33.6	5	168.0
3	16.3	3	48.9	4	195.6
4	17.5	2	35.0	3	105.0
5	14.4	3	43.2	2	86.4
6	8.7	3	26.1	1	26.1
7	3.0	1	3.0	0	0

Sum of the products   191.1 Sum of products   588.9
        for area   for moment

Distance of geometrical centre from aft $= \dfrac{\text{Sum of the products for moment} \times h}{\text{Sum of the products for area}}$

$$= \frac{588.9 \times 36}{191.1} = 110.94 \text{ metres}$$

3.   Using the 1st Rule and taking moments about the middle ordinate.

No. of ordinate	½ ordinate	x S.M.	= Product for area	x lever	= Product for moment
1	1.3	1	1.3	3	3.9
2	11.2	4	44.8	2	89.6
3	16.3	2	32.6	1	32.6
4	17.5	4	70.0	0	126.1 Forward
5	14.4	2	28.8	1	28.8
6	8.7	4	34.8	2	69.6
7	3.0	1	3.0	3	9.0

			Sum of products for area	Resultant product for moment	
			215.3	107.4 Aft	
				18.7 Forward	

$$
\text{Distance of the geometrical centre from the middle ordinate} = \frac{\text{Resultant product for moment} \times h}{\text{Sum of the products for area}}
$$

$$
= \frac{18.7 \times 36}{215.3}
$$

$$
= 3.127 \text{ metres forward}
$$

The use of the 3rd. Rule enables the geometrical centre of an area between two adjacent ordinates to be found if an additional ordinate is known. The multipliers 3, 10 and -1 are used for this purpose in order to find the moment of area.

To use: Determine the area under consideration using Simpson's 3rd. Rule. Then:

To 3 times the ordinate bounding the area add 10 times the middle ordinate, subtract the other given ordinate and multiply this result by $\frac{1}{24}$ of the square of the common interval.

So given semi-ordinates y, y_1, and y_2

Moment ABCD $= \frac{h^2}{24} (3y + 10y_1 - y_2) \times 2$

Distance of CG along PQ from P

$= \frac{\text{Moment}}{\text{Area}}$

Similarly:-

Moment CDEF $= \frac{h^2}{24} (3y_2 + 10y_1 - y) \times 2$

Distance of CG along QP from Q

$= \frac{\text{Moment}}{\text{Area}}$

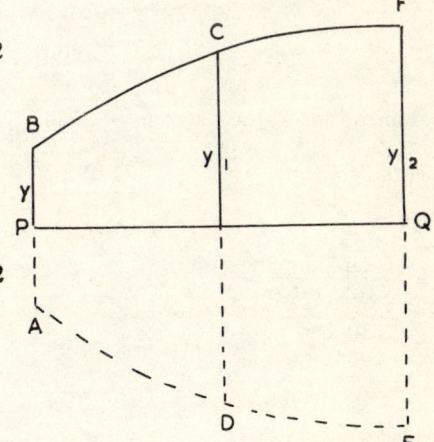

WORKED EXAMPLE 9

The following semi-ordinates are spaced at 20 metre intervals, 7.7, 12.5 and 17.3 metres. Find the deck area between each ordinate and the position of the geometrical centre of each area.

Area between 1st and 2nd ordinates.

½ Ord	x	S.M.	=	Product for Area
7.7		5		38.5
12.5		8		100.0
17.3		- 1		- 17.3
				138.5
				- 17.3

Sum of products for area   121.2

$$\frac{1}{12}h \quad = \quad \frac{20}{12} \quad x \quad \frac{5}{3}$$

½ area   202

$$\text{Area} = 202 \text{ x } 2 \text{ m}^2$$
$$= 404 \text{ m}^2$$

Area between 2nd and 3rd ordinates.

½ Ord	x	S.M.	=	Product for Area
17.3		5		86.5
12.5		8		100.0
7.7		- 1		- 7.7
				186.5
				- 7.7

Sum of products for area   178.8

$$\frac{1}{12}h \quad = \quad \frac{20}{12} \quad x \quad \frac{5}{3}$$

½ area   298

$$\text{Area} = 298 \text{ x } 2 \text{ m}^2$$
$$= 596 \text{ m}^2$$

To find geometrical centres.

½ Ord	x	S.M.	=	Product for moments
7.7		3		23.1
12.5		10		125.0
17.3		- 1		- 17.3
				148.1
				- 17.3
				130.8

$$\frac{h^2}{24} = \frac{400}{24} \quad x \quad \frac{400}{24}$$

Moment for ½ area   2180

Total Moments   2180 x 2

Distance of CG from 7.7 ordinate

$$= \frac{\text{Total Moments}}{\text{Total Area}}$$

$$= \frac{2180 \text{ x } 2}{404} = 10.792 \text{ metres}$$

½ Ord.	x	S.M.	=	Product for moments
17.3		3		51.9
12.5		10		125.0
7.7		- 1		7.7
				176.9
				- 7.7
				169.2

$$\frac{h^2}{24} = \frac{400}{24} \quad x \quad \frac{400}{24}$$

Moment for ½ area   2820

Total Moments   2820 x 2

Distance of CG from 17.3 ordinate

$$= \frac{\text{Total Moments}}{\text{Total Area}}$$

$$= \frac{2820 \text{ x } 2}{596} = 9.463 \text{ metres}$$

In the examples so far, a series of ordinates has been given; after putting these through Simpson's Rules an area is obtained.

If a series of areas is now put through Simpson's Rules a volume is obtained. The geometrical centre of a volume may be found in a similar manner to that of an area.

WORKED EXAMPLE 10
The areas of equidistantly spaced vertical sections of a vessel's underwater form 400 metres long and starting from forward are as follows:- 30, 226.4, 487.8, 731.6, 883.0, 825.5, 587.2, 262.1 and 39.8 square metres respectively. Calculate her displacement in salt water and the longitudinal position of the centre of buoyancy.

Section No.	Area	x S.M.	=	Product for volume	x Lever	=	Product for Moment
1	30	1		30.0	4		120.0
2	226.4	4		905.6	3		2716.8
3	487.8	2		975.6	2		1951.2
4	731.6	4		2926.4	1		2926.4
5	883.0	2		1766.0	0		7714.4 F
6	825.5	4		3302.0	1		3302.0
7	587.2	2		1174.4	2		2348.8
8	262.1	4		1048.4	3		3145.2
9	39.8	1		39.8	4		159.2

Sum of the products for volume   12168.2   8955.2 A

$$\frac{1}{3}h = \frac{(50)}{3} \quad x \quad \frac{50}{3} \quad \text{Resultant product for moment} \quad 1240.8 \text{ A}$$

Volume 202803.3m^3

Displacement tonnes   =   202803.3 x 1.025

                       =   207873.4 tonnes

Distance of C.B. from midlength   = $\dfrac{\text{Sum of the products for moments x h}}{\text{Sum of the products for volume}}$

                                   = $\dfrac{1240.8 \times 50}{12168.2}$

                                   =   5.098 metres abaft midlength

Instead of giving waterplane areas, the TPC is often given for the various draughts.

WORKED EXAMPLE 11

The following is an extract from a vessel's hydrostatic table.

Draught	7m	8m	9m	10m	11m	12m	13m	14m
TPC	43.1	43.6	44.1	44.6	45.0	45.4	45.8	46.2

The displacement at a draught of 7m is 15000 tonnes. Calculate the displacement at a draught of 14m and the position of the centre of buoyancy at this draught if the KB is 4.6m at 7.0m draught.

Draught	TPC	x S.M. =	Product for volume	x Lever	= Product for moment
14	46.2	1	46.2	4	184.8
13	45.8	4	183.2	3	549.6
12	45.4	2	90.8	2	181.6
11	45.0	4	180.0	1	180.0
10	44.6	1 1	44.6 44.6	0 3	0 133.8
9	44.1	3	132.3	2	264.6
8	43.6	3	130.8	1	130.8
7	43.1	1	43.1	0	0
			544.8 350.8		1096.0 529.2

$$1 \text{ x } \frac{1}{3} \qquad 1 \text{ x } \frac{3}{8}$$

$$\frac{181.6}{100} \qquad \frac{131.55}{100}$$

$$\frac{}{18160} \qquad \frac{}{13155}$$

$$TPC = \frac{1.025A}{100}$$

$$\therefore A = \frac{100TPC}{1.025}$$

Putting TPC through the rules and multiplying by $\frac{100}{1.025}$ V would be obtained
Now W tonnes = V x 1.025 (for salt water) ∴ if we multiply directly by 100 we get the same result.

Displacement between 7 and 14m   31315 tonnes

Appendage   15000 tonnes

Total Displacement upto 14m   =   46315 tonnes

Distance of CB of upper portion

above 10m W.L.   = $\dfrac{1096.0 \times 1}{544.8}$ =   2.0117m

or   12.0117m above the keel.

Distance of CB of lower portion

above 7m W.L.   = $\dfrac{529.2 \times 1}{350.8}$ =   1.5086m

or   8.5086m above the keel.

As Displacement is proportional to Volume

Displacement	x	KBs	=	Moment
18160		12.0117		218132
13155		8.5086		111931
15000		4.6000		69000
46315				399063

KB of total volume   = $\dfrac{399063}{46315}$ =   8.616m

Check by MORRISH'S Formula

$$KB = d - \frac{1}{3}\left(\frac{d}{2} + \frac{V}{A}\right)$$

$$= 14 - \frac{1}{3}\left(\frac{14}{2} + \frac{46315}{1.025} \times \frac{1.025}{46.2 \times 100}\right)$$

$$= 8.325 \text{ metres}$$

WORKED EXAMPLE 12

From the following information calculate the vessel's deadweight carrying capacity.

Light draught	8.0m	Waterplane Area	9750m^2
,, ,,	10.0m	,, ,,	11278m^2
,, ,,	12.0m	,, ,,	12600m^2
Load draught	14.0m	,, ,,	13925m^2

Waterplane area	x	S.M.	=	Product for volume
9750		1		9750
11278		3		33834
12600		3		37800
13925		1		13925
				95309

$$\frac{3}{8}h = 2 \times \frac{3}{8} \times \frac{.75}{}$$

$$\text{Volume} \qquad 71481.75\text{m}^3$$

$$\text{Deadweight carrying capacity} = 71481.75 \times 1.025$$

$$= \underline{73269 \text{ tonnes}}$$

CHAPTER THREE

Ship Stresses

In chapter one it was shown that the total weight of the ship and contents is equal to the total upthrust due to buoyancy if the vessel is to float. However, although the weight is considered to act vertically downwards through the centre of gravity, this total is composed of many individual weights which act at many different parts of the ship.

The total upthrust due to buoyancy is considered to act vertically upwards through the centre of buoyancy but this total upthrust is composed of countless individual upthrusts acting on the plating of the ship.

If the downward force due to weight at a point and the upward thrust due to buoyancy at the same point are not equal, stresses will occur. These stresses can be expressed as Shear Forces and Bending Moments. Steps taken to counteract their effects are detailed in the companion volume "Ship Construction Sketches and Notes".

Whilst finding these shear forces and bending moments in practice is a somewhat complicated exercise, the theory is similar to that of shear forces and bending moments on a beam, and these are first considered.

SHEAR FORCE
When a section such as a beam is carrying a load there is a tendency for some parts to be pushed upwards and for other parts to move downwards, this tendency is termed shearing. The shear force at a point or station is the vertical force at that point. The shear force at a station may also be defined as being the total load on either the left hand side or the right hand side of the station: load being defined as the difference between the downward and upward forces.

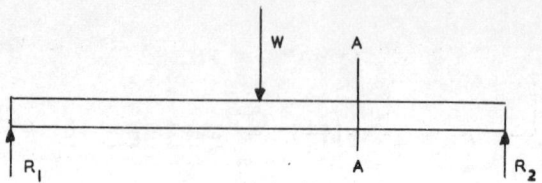

If the beam shown above is static and supported at its ends, the total forces upwards (reaction at the pivots) must equal the downward forces (loads).

$$R_1 + R_2 = W \ldots \ldots \ldots \ldots .1$$

To the left of the line AA there is a resultant downward force $W - R_1$
To the right of the line AA there is an upward force R_2
The shear force at a point on the beam along AA is either $W - R_1$ or R_2
It can be seen from 1 above that these two quantities are the same.

BENDING MOMENT
The beam which we have been considering would also have a tendency to bend and the bending moment measures this tendency. Its size depends on the amount of the load as well as how the load is placed together with the method of support. Bending moments are calculated in the same way as ordinary moments i.e. multiplying force by distance, and so they are expressed in weight-length units. As with the calculation of shear force the bending moment at a station is obtained by considering moments either to the left or the right of the station.

In the diagrams on subsequent pages shear forces and bending moments are drawn in accordance with the understated sign convention. "If a downward force (weight loaded) is considered negative and a reaction or upthrust considered positive then the shear force is measured upwards from the zero line if loads to the left of the station result in a positive shear force, or if loads to the right of the station result in a negative shear force. The force is measured downward from the zero line if the opposite signs result". A positive shear is illustrated for point X in the sketch below. "Bending moments will likewise be positive or negative and a positive moment resulting from consideration of loads either to the left or to the right of the station is measured below the zero line and a negative moment resulting from consideration of loads is measured above the line". Positive moments cause sagging and are illustrated in the sketch at the top of page 29.

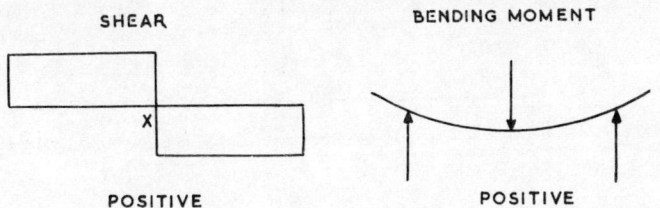

SHEAR

BENDING MOMENT

X

POSITIVE

POSITIVE

In the following theory it is sometimes convenient to consider a point as being an infinitesimal distance to the left or right of the station at which the shear force or bending moment is required. Such a position is suffixed with the letter $_L$ or $_R$.

A HORIZONTAL BEAM WITH END SUPPORTS

a) Weightless with a point load at the centre

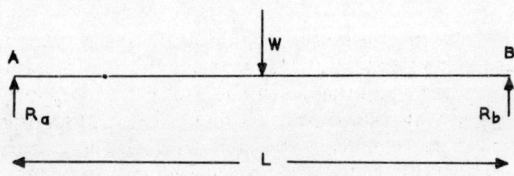

If stationary, $W = R_a + R_b$

To find R_a and R_b.

Taking moments about A.

Anti-clockwise moments   =   Clockwise moments.

$$R_b \times L \qquad = \qquad W \times \frac{L}{2}$$

$$R_b \qquad = \qquad \frac{W}{2}$$

If pivot B supports half the weight the rest must be supported at A.

Therefore $R_a \qquad = \qquad \frac{W}{2}$

Station	Shear Force	Bending Moment
A_R	R_a or $\dfrac{W}{2}$	0
¼L	R_a or $\dfrac{W}{2}$	$\dfrac{W}{2} \times \dfrac{L}{4} = \dfrac{WL}{8}$
½L$_L$	R_a or $\dfrac{W}{2}$	$\dfrac{W}{2} \times \dfrac{L}{2} = \dfrac{WL}{4}$
½L$_R$	$R_a - W = -\dfrac{W}{2}$	$\dfrac{W}{2} \times \dfrac{L}{2} = \dfrac{WL}{4}$

It may be noted that the shear forces and bending moments shown above have been obtained by considering loads and moments to the left of the stations. Exactly the same results would have been obtained if loads and moments to the right of the stations had been considered, these are shown below. The reason for the different signs in the shear forces will be apparent from reference to the text on Page 28.

Station	Shear Force	Bending Moment
A	$R_b - W = -\dfrac{W}{2}$	$\left(\dfrac{W}{2} \times L\right) - \left(W \times \dfrac{L}{2}\right) = 0$
¼L	$R_b - W = \dfrac{W}{2}$	$\left(\dfrac{W}{2} \times \dfrac{3L}{4}\right) - \left(W \times \dfrac{L}{4}\right) = \dfrac{WL}{8}$
½L$_L$	$R_b - W = -\dfrac{W}{2}$	$\dfrac{W}{2} \times \dfrac{L}{2} = \dfrac{WL}{4}$
½L$_R$	$R_b = \dfrac{W}{2}$	$\dfrac{W}{2} \times \dfrac{L}{2} = \dfrac{WL}{4}$

The foregoing theory should emphasise that the shear force at a point is found by the algebraic summing of the loads **either** to the left **or** the right of that point. Likewise the bending moment at a station is the algebraic sum of the moments either to the left or the right of the station.

If the convention shown on page 28 is used the shear forces and bending moments could be plotted on a diagram as shown below.

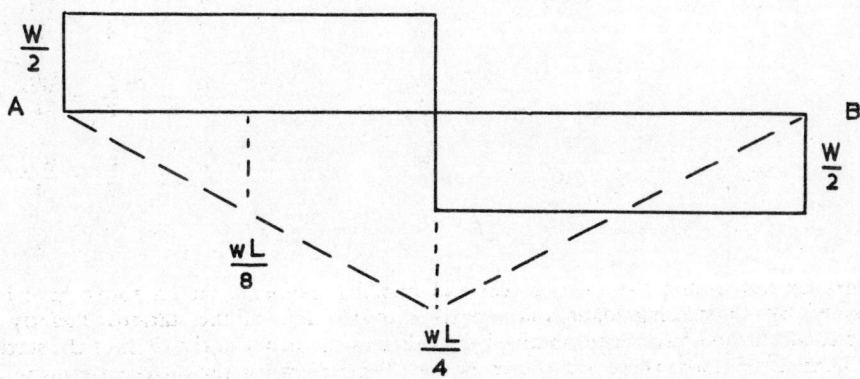

NOTE: Both the tables on page 30 and the figure above show that the area under the shear force curve upto a point is equal to the bending moment at that point.

b)   Weightless with an evenly spread load. This has exactly the same effect as a beam of uniform section whose weight is distributed uniformly along the beam

If the total load is W and the length is L, then the weight per unit length w equals $\frac{W}{L}$.

Reaction $R_a = R_b = \frac{W}{2}$

Station	Shear Force	Bending Moment
A_R	$R_a = \dfrac{W}{2}$	0
¼L	$R_a - \dfrac{wL}{4}$	$\dfrac{W}{2} \times \dfrac{L}{4} - \dfrac{wL}{4} \times \dfrac{L}{8}$
	or $\dfrac{W}{2} - \dfrac{W}{4} = \dfrac{W}{4}$	or $\dfrac{WL}{8} - \dfrac{WL}{32} = \dfrac{3WL}{32}$
½L	$R_a - \dfrac{wL}{2}$	$\dfrac{W}{2} \times \dfrac{L}{2} - \dfrac{wL}{2} \times \dfrac{L}{4}$
	or $\dfrac{W}{2} - \dfrac{W}{2} = 0$	or $\dfrac{WL}{4} - \dfrac{WL}{8} = \dfrac{WL}{8}$
B	$R_a - wL$	$\dfrac{W}{2} \times L - wL \times \dfrac{L}{2}$
	or $\dfrac{W}{2} - W = \dfrac{W}{2}$	or $\dfrac{WL}{2} - \dfrac{WL}{2} = 0$

The above have been obtained by considering loads and bending moments to the left of each station. It is suggested that the reader now considers the loads and bending moments to the right of each station. The values of the shear forces and bending moments so found will be exactly the same as those above.

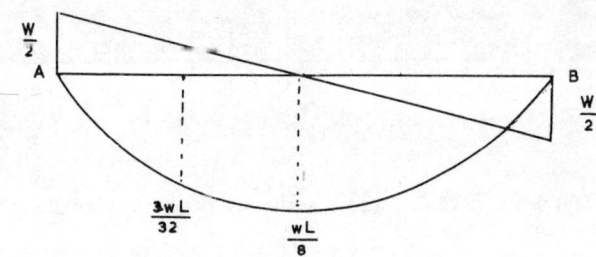

The shear force and bending moment diagram shown above will be typical of any uniformly loaded beam.

c)   A beam having an unevenly spread load.

In this case a curve of loads would be drawn, each ordinate representing the average load per unit length at that part of the beam. The general principles already described can then be followed namely that the shear force at any point of the beam is the resultant of the upthrusts and loads on one side of that point. The bending moment at any point can be obtained by finding the area under the shear force curve up to that point. Worked example 14 shows how this is done in the case of a ship.

WORKED EXAMPLE 13

A uniform beam AB 6 metres in length and weight 3 tonnes is supported at its ends. Weights of 1 tonne and 2 tonnes are loaded at points 2 metres and 5 metres from the end A. Calculate the shear force at a point 4 metres from A and the bending moment 1.5 metres from A.

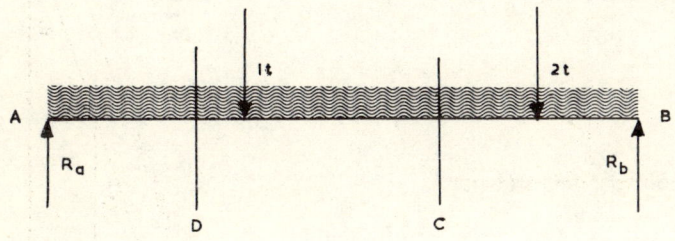

Weight of the beam is 3 tonnes or 0.5 tonne per metre

To find the reactions at A and B

The total moment about any point caused by the reactions

$\qquad$ = The total moment about that point caused by the loads.

Taking moments about A

$$R_a \times 0 + R_b \times 6 \quad = \quad 3 \times 3 + 1 \times 2 + 2 \times 5$$

$$R_b \quad = \quad \frac{21}{6} \quad = \quad 3.5 \text{ tonnes}$$

$$R_a + R_b \quad = \quad 6.0 \text{ tonnes}$$

$$R_a \quad = \quad 2.5 \text{ tonnes}$$

Let C be the point 4 metres from A
Consider loads to the left of C

Part weight of beam 0.5 x 4	=	- 2 tonnes
Load		- 1 tonne
Reaction at A (R_a)		2.5 tonnes
Shear force at C		- 0.5 tonne

Check by considering loads to the right of C

Part weight of beam 0.5 x 2	=	- 1 tonne
Load		- 2 tonnes
Reaction at B (R_b)		3.5 tonnes
Shear force at C		0.5 tonne

Let D be the point 1.5 metres from A

Consider loads and distances to the left of point D

Reaction at A (R_a) causes a moment of 2.5 x 1.5	= 3.75 t-m
Weight of beam from D to A " " - 0.5 x 1.5 x 0.75	= - 0.5625 t-m
Bending moment	3.1875 t-m

Check by considering loads and distances to the right of point D

Reaction at B (R_b) causes a moment of 3.5 x 4.5	= 15.75 t-m
Weight of beam from D to B " " - 0.5 x 4.5 x 2.25	= - 5.0625 t-m
Weight of 1 tonne	- 1.0 x 0.5	= - 0.5 t-m
Weight of 2 tonnes	- 2.0 x 3.5	= - 7.0 t-m
Bending moment	3.1875 t-m

It is suggested that the reader calculates the shear forces and bending moments at points 0.5m apart between A and B. The shear force diagram could then be drawn - this should appear as shown below - and the bending moments checked from the diagram, remembering that the area under the shear force diagram either to the left or to the right of the station where the bending moment is required gives the bending moment.

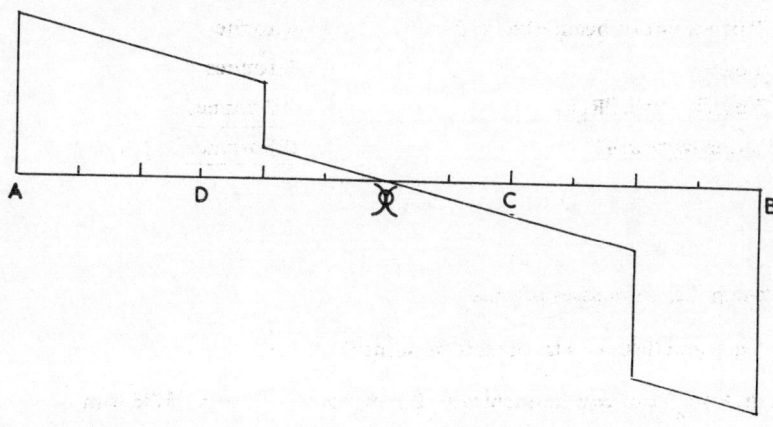

It can be seen from an analysis of the above diagram that it contains three features:-

i)   The greatest Bending Moment occurs at midlength.

ii)   There is a sharp discontinuity at the points where there are concentrated loads. This is similar to the shear curve for the weightless beam with point loading.

iii)   There is a gradual slope where the load is uniformly distributed. This is similar to the weightless beam with a uniform load.

The greatest value of the shear curve is that it shows the position of maximum bending moment.

So far beams supported at each end have been considered. If a beam is not supported at the extreme ends different problems arise in calculating shear forces and bending moments beyond the points of support although the general theory is the same.

The part of the beam beyond the end support may be considered as a cantilever which is a beam with one end fixed and the other end free. Shear forces and bending moments for two conditions of loading a cantilever follow.

When calculating shear forces and bending moments at a station in the case of a cantilever beam the loads to be considered should be those from the station towards the free end of the beam. If the free end is always considered as being to the right then the sign convention on page 28 is applicable.

a)   Weightless with point loading at the free end.

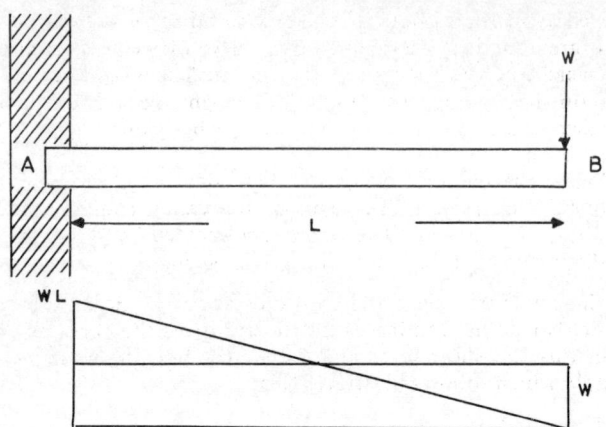

Station	Shear force	Bending Moment
B$_L$	- W	0
½L	- W	$-\dfrac{WL}{2}$
A	- W	- WL

b)   Weightless, with evenly spread load.

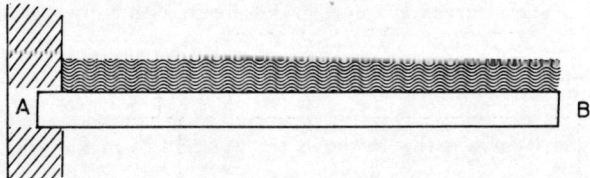

Weight per foot run w equals $\dfrac{W}{L}$

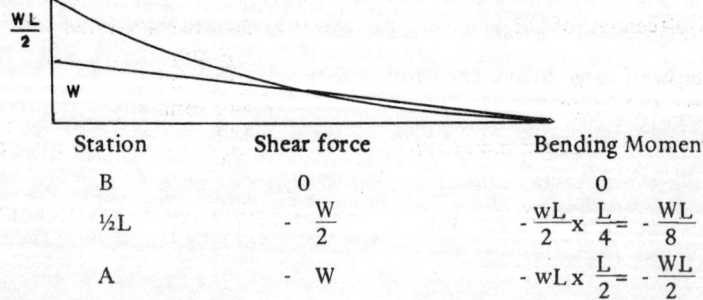

Station	Shear force	Bending Moment
B	0	0
½L	$-\dfrac{W}{2}$	$-\dfrac{wL}{2} \times \dfrac{L}{4} = -\dfrac{WL}{8}$
A	- W	$- wL \times \dfrac{L}{2} = -\dfrac{WL}{2}$

APPLICATION TO SHIPS

As ships may be considered as a form of beam the theory so far discussed can be applied. The loads along the ship are found by first plotting a curve of weights, each ordinate representing the average weight per unit length at that point. The weight per unit length would vary dependent upon the loading - the greater the weight the shorter the distance. A second curve is then drawn, this is the curve of upthrusts or buoyancy.

Each of the curves can vary, the curve of weights is dependent on the type of loading (light or loaded conditions for example). The curve of buoyancy could be drawn for either the still water condition or for when the vessel is supported by waves at the ends (sagging) or when she is supported by a wave at midlength (hogging).

The difference between the curves of weight and buoyancy at any point is the load which is drawn as an ordinate at that point. Joining each ordinate gives the curve of loads and from the information on this the shear force and thence the bending moments can be found. The worked example which follows illustrates this.

WORKED EXAMPLE 14

A box shaped barge, length 30m, breadth 8m and depth 6m, floats at an even keel draught to 4m in saltwater of relative density 1.025, has 500 tonnes of ore spread over the midship half-length and two cases of machinery each weighing 20 tonnes, measuring 2m x 2m x 2m, stowed on the centre line 5m from each end.

Construct a curve of loads for the still water condition assuming the weight of the barge to be evenly distributed over the full length and from it draw curves for Shear Force and Bending Moments.

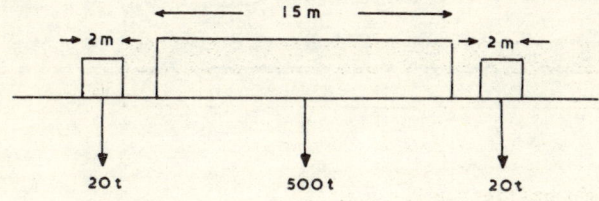

Displacement of barge	=	$30 \times 8 \times 4 \times 1.025$		
	=	984 tonnes		
Weight of cargo	=	540 tonnes		
Weight of barge	=	444 tonnes		
Weight of barge per metre run	=	$\dfrac{444}{30}$	=	14.8 tonnes
Buoyancy per metre run	=	$\dfrac{984}{30}$	=	32.8 tonnes
Ore spread " " "	=	$\dfrac{500}{15}$	=	33.3 tonnes
Machinery spread "	=	$\dfrac{20}{2}$	=	10.0 tonnes

Keeping to the convention on page 28 the buoyancy per metre run is laid off upwards from the datum line AB and is represented by rectangle ABCD. Weight reduces the effect of buoyancy so that it is laid off downwards from line CD. The weight per metre run of the ship is represented by CE and the weight of the ship by rectangle CDEF. The weights of the cargo will further reduce the effect of buoyancy and these are laid downwards from EF in their appropriate fore and aft positions being represented by rectangles GIJH, KMNL and OQRP. The portion of the buoyancy curve which is intact above AB represents positive loads and the weight curve below AB represents negative loads. The load curve is now drawn and is shown as a dotted line.

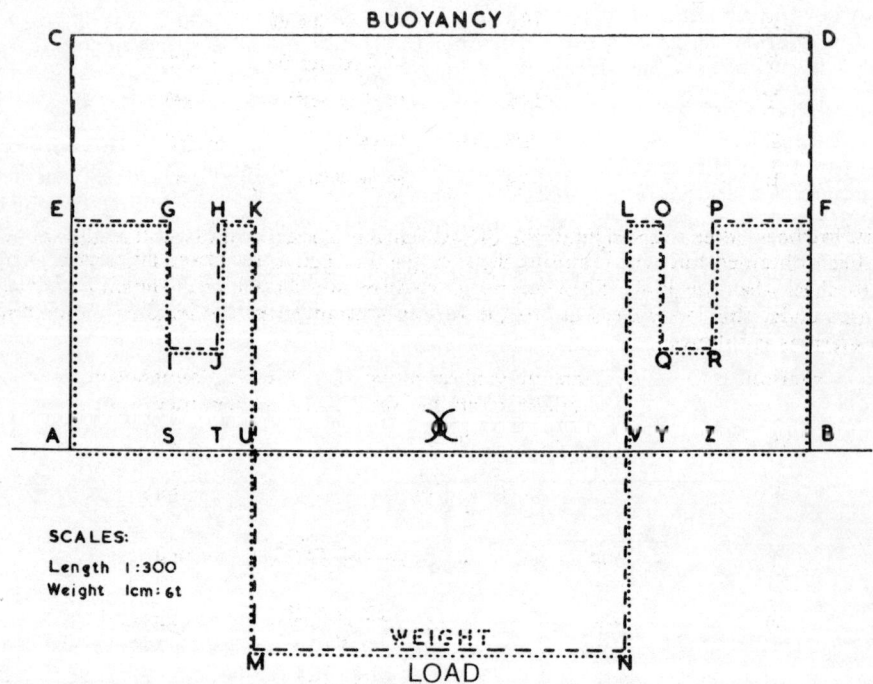

The method outlined above is very suitable for the still water condition where buoyancy is evenly distributed. For such a vessel in a seaway and in more complicated work both buoyancy and weight are laid off from the baseline AB.

Summing the loads to the left or right at the various stations gives the shear force at those points. The summing of the loads is done by obtaining the area under the curve of loads up to the station, as the ordinates of the load curve are weights per metre run, if these are multiplied by the distance between them a load is obtained. This load is in weight units as $\frac{W}{L} \times L = W$

Station	Area under load curve to left of station			Shear force in tonnes
A		0		0
S	(4	x	18)	72
T	72	+	(2 x 8)	88
U	88	+	(1.5 x 18)	115
X	115	-	(7.5 x 15.3)	0
V	0	-	(7.5 x 15.3)	- 115
Y	- 115	+	(1.5 x 18)	- 88
Z	- 88	+	(2 x 8)	- 72
B	- 72	+	(4 x 18)	0

If areas had been taken to the right of the various stations the same numerical results would have been obtained but with opposite signs as per the sign convention. The reader may care to check that this is so. The shear force curve is now drawn with the above values. The area under this latter curve up to the various stations gives the bending moment at those stations as follows:

Station	Area under shear curve to left of the station			Bending Moment in tonnes metres
A		0		0
S		$4(\frac{0 + 72}{2})$		144
T	144	+	$2(\frac{72 + 88}{2})$	304
U	304	+	$1.5(\frac{88 + 115}{2})$	456.25
X	456.25	+	$7.5(\frac{115 + 0}{2})$	887.5
V	887.5	-	$7.5(\frac{0 + 115}{2})$	456.25
Y	456.25	-	$1.5(\frac{115 + 88}{2})$	304
Z	304	-	$2(\frac{88 + 72}{2})$	144
B	144	-	$4(\frac{72 + 0}{2})$	0

The same results would have been obtained by taking moments to the right of the stations.

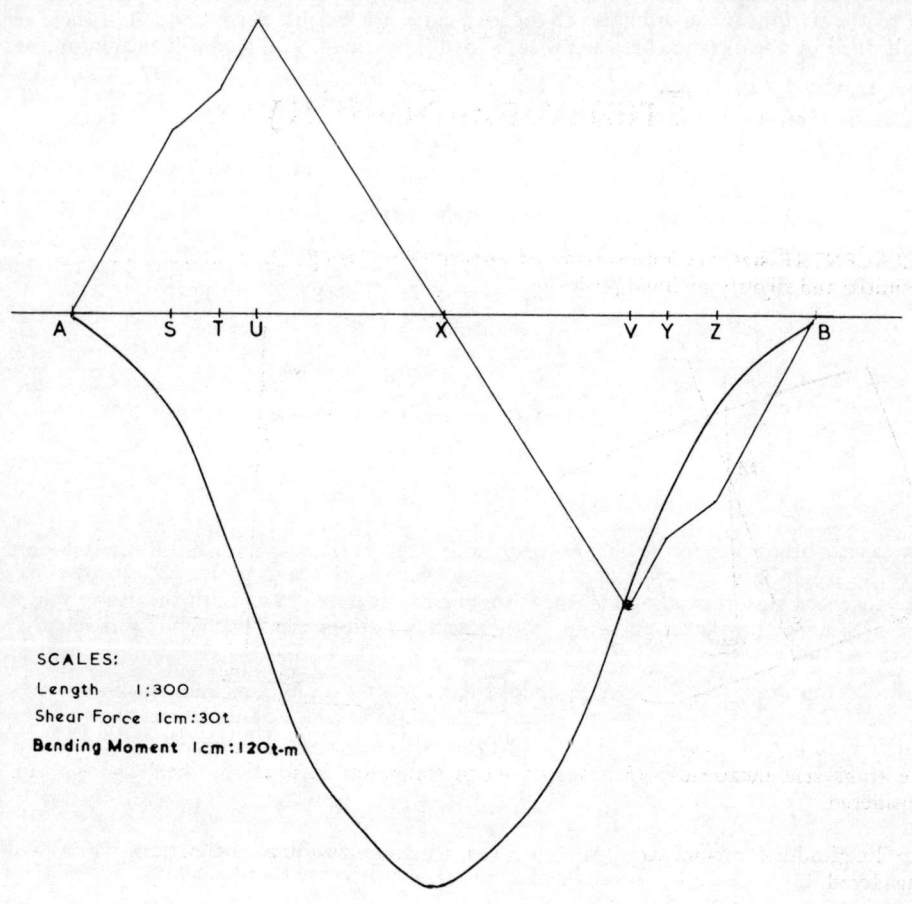

SCALES:

Length   1:300

Shear Force   1cm:30t

Bending Moment   1cm:120t-m

The resulting curve of bending moments is shown on the diagram above.

The maximum bending moment is seen to occur at midlength and as this is a positive moment it gives a sagging condition.

CHAPTER FOUR

Transverse Stability

METACENTRE is at the intersection of vertical lines through the centres of buoyancy in the initial and slightly inclined positions.

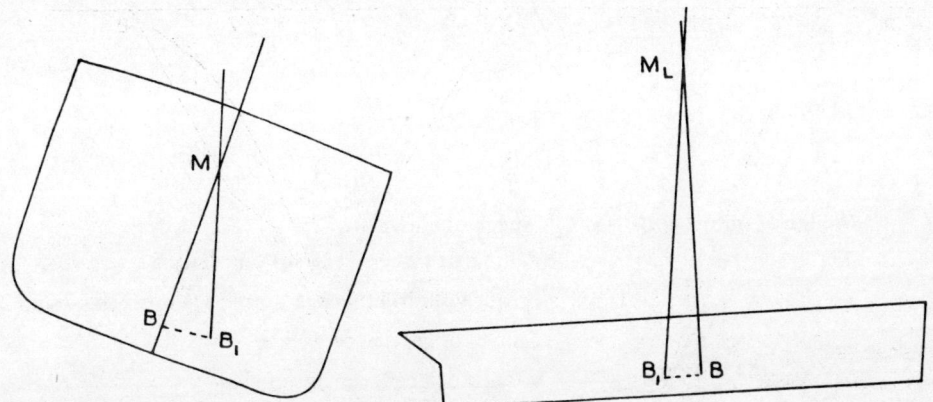

The transverse metacentre (M) is used when transverse inclinations (heel and list) are considered.

The longitudinal metacentre (M_L) is used when longitudinal inclinations (trim) are considered.

METACENTRIC HEIGHT (GM) is the distance between the centre of gravity and the metacentre.

The position of the metacentre may be calculated from the formula.

$$BM = \frac{I}{V}$$ the proof of which is shown below

I is the moment of inertia of the waterplane in metre^4 units.
V is the volume of displacement in cubic metres.

NOTE: The moment of inertia, which is also called the second moment of area, of a body about a line can be obtained by multiplying the mass of each and every particle in the body by the square of its distance from the line about which the moment of inertia is required. Adding the quantity found for each and every particle in the body gives the moment of inertia of the body.

TO PROVE BM $= \dfrac{I}{V}$

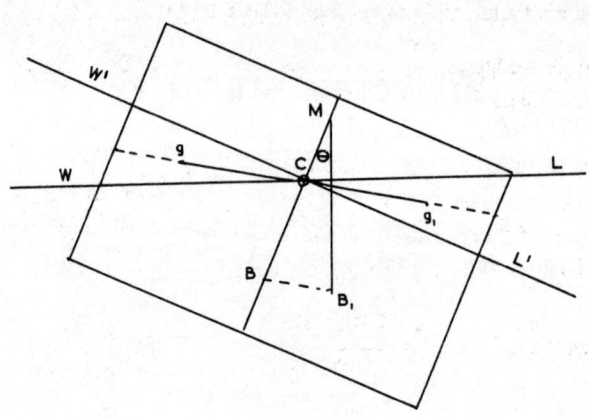

Wedge of immersion	=	Wedge of emersion
Let v	=	volume of either wedge of unit length
b	=	breadth of either wedge = ½ breadth of ship
g and g_1	=	centres of gravity of wedges
V	=	volume of displacement of ship

then BB_1 $\qquad = \qquad \dfrac{v \ \times \ gg_1}{V}$

Let the angle of heel θ be infinitely small so it can be said that WC, W^1C, LC, L^1C are all equal in length and triangles WCW^1 and LCL^1 are isosceles.

Now area of triangle WCW^1 $\quad = \quad$ ½ $b^2 \sin \theta$ Note: $WW^1 = b \sin\theta$

Distance gg_1 $\qquad = \qquad \dfrac{4}{3} CL^1$ or $\dfrac{4}{3} b$

The moment of area $\qquad = \qquad \dfrac{b^2}{2} \sin \theta \times \dfrac{4}{3} b \quad = \quad \dfrac{2b^3}{3} \sin \theta$

If we consider a triangle of infinitely small length which we will call unity (1) then this moment is also the moment of the volume of the wedge at this particular point only. We must take the volume of all the other wedges and sum them up by integration or putting them through Simpson's Rules, the summation is denoted by Σ

Moment of whole wedge $\quad = \quad v \times gg_1 \quad = \quad \Sigma \dfrac{2b^3}{3} \sin \theta$

θ being very small $\dfrac{BB_1}{BM} \quad = \quad \sin \theta$

$\qquad\qquad\qquad BB_1 \quad = \quad BM \sin \theta$

Now $\qquad\qquad BB_1 \quad = \quad \dfrac{v \times gg_1}{V} \quad = \quad \dfrac{\Sigma \frac{2}{3} b^3 \sin \theta}{V}$

$BM \sin \theta \quad = \quad \dfrac{\Sigma \frac{2}{3} b^3 \sin \theta}{V}$

$BM \quad = \quad \dfrac{\Sigma \frac{2}{3} b^3 \sin \theta}{\sin \theta \times V} \quad = \quad \dfrac{\Sigma \frac{2}{3} b^3}{V}$

But $\Sigma \frac{2}{3} b^3$ is, from the above work and by definition, the moment of inertia of the waterplane (I).

$$\therefore \quad BM \quad = \quad \frac{I}{V}$$

If the BM's are known a curve of metacentres can be drawn by plotting metacentric heights against draughts, an example for a box-shaped vessel follows. In a box shape I and V can be readily calculated as

I for a rectangular waterplane is $\dfrac{LB^3}{12}$ for transverse inclinations

or $\dfrac{BL^3}{12}$ for longitudinal inclinations

The volume of displacement of a boxshape is $L \times B \times d$

Hence for boxshape $BM \quad = \quad \dfrac{LB^3}{12 \times L \times B \times d} \quad = \quad \dfrac{B^2}{12d}$ (transversely)

$\qquad\qquad\qquad\qquad\qquad\qquad\qquad\qquad$ or $\qquad \dfrac{L^2}{12d}$ (longitudinally)

For a triangular shape $\qquad\qquad\qquad BM \quad = \quad \dfrac{B^2}{6\,d}$ (transversely)

$\qquad\qquad\qquad\qquad\qquad\qquad\qquad\qquad$ or $\qquad \dfrac{L^2}{6\,d}$ (longitudinally)

In all cases   L is the length of the waterplane
$\qquad\qquad\quad$ B is the breadth of the waterplane
$\qquad\qquad\quad$ d is the draught

WORKED EXAMPLE 15

Draw a curve of metacentres for a boxshaped vessel 270m in length, 24m in breadth, 17m in depth.

Draught	BM	KB	KM (all in metres)
0	oo	0	oo
1	48	.5	48.5
2	24	1.0	25.0
3	16	1.5	17.5
4	12	2.0	14.0
5	9.6	2.5	12.1
6	8.0	3.0	11.0
7	6.8	3.5	10.3
8	6.0	4.0	10.0
9	5.3	4.5	9.8
10	4.8	5.0	9.8
11	4.4	5.5	9.9
12	4.0	6.0	10.0
13	3.7	6.5	10.2
14	3.4	7.0	10.4

The KM's are now plotted against draughts. In the first curve shown the scales for draught and KM are different. In the second curve a 45^0 line is used, making the scales the same.

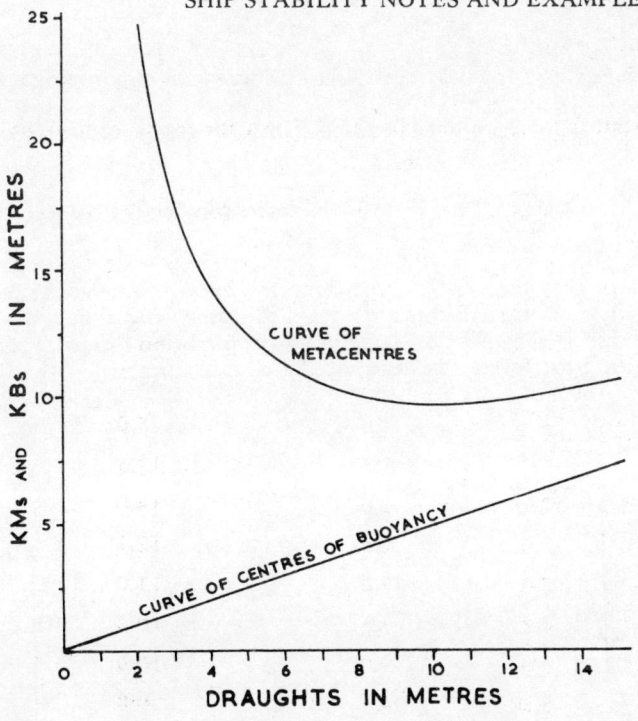

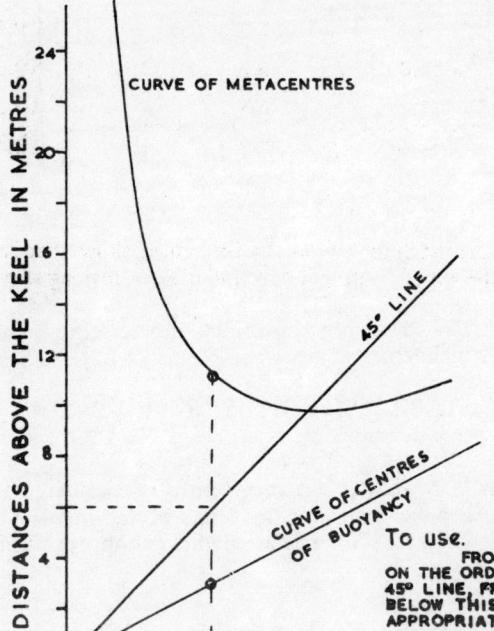

To use.

FROM THE REQUIRED DRAUGHT ON THE ORDINATE COME ACROSS TO THE 45° LINE, FROM THE KEEL DIRECTLY BELOW THIS POINT MEASURE UP THE APPROPRIATE DISTANCE. THE PLOT FOR 6 METRES DRAUGHT IS SHOWN.

A COUPLE is formed when two equal parallel forces are acting in opposite directions.

THE LEVER OF A COUPLE is the perpendicular distance between the forces forming the couple.

MOMENT OF A COUPLE is the product of one of the forces forming the couple and the lever of the couple.

It has already been shown that the vessel's weight and the force of buoyancy must be equal for the vessel to float. If these forces are not on the same vertical line they will form a couple. Such a case is shown below, a righting couple being formed when the vessel is heeled by the external force. The lever of the couple is known as the GZ or RIGHTING LEVER.

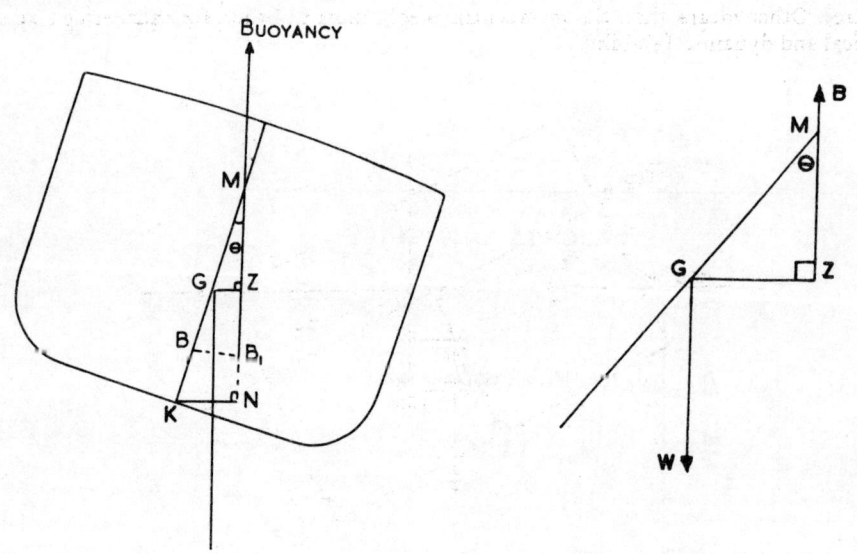

STABILITY or STATICAL STABILITY is the ability of a vessel to return to her initial position after being forcibly inclined.

MOMENT OF STATICAL STABILITY or RIGHTING MOMENT is a measure of the vessel's ability to return to her initial position. It is always W x GZ tonnes-metres.

METACENTRIC STABILITY. With this the metacentre is considered as being a fixed point. The GZ lever can then be expressed in terms of the metacentric height, i.e. GZ = GM sine θ (this is only true for angles of inclination upto about 15^{0}).

As GM   =   KM - KG

GM sin θ =   (KM - KG) sin θ =   KM sin θ -   KG sin θ

KM sin θ =   KN

so GM sin θ can be expressed as KN - KG sin θ (see stability curves on page 101).

INITIAL STABILITY is the stability of the vessel in her initial position and is expressed by the metacentric height.

DYNAMICAL STABILITY is the measure of the work which is done when the vessel is inclined by external forces. It may be found by multiplying the vertical separation of B ang G by the displacement. For angles upto 15° it is approximately W x GM x 2 haversine θ. Another method of calculating this is shown on page 103.

STABILITY AT THE LARGER ANGLES.
The metacentre can no longer be considered fixed (it is known now as the pro-meta-centre). Other means than the metacentric height must be found for calculating a vessel's statical and dynamical stability.

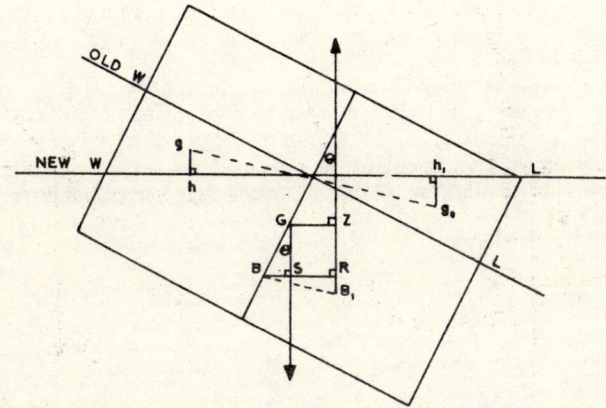

When a vessel of volume V heels, there is a transference of buoyancy from one side to another. In the above figure, g and g_1 are the centres of gravity of the emersed and immersed volumes or wedges of buoyancy, the volume of each being v.

The centre of buoyancy will move to B_1 (as the underwater shape has changed) and

$$BB_1 = \frac{v \times gg_1}{V}$$

BB_1 is parallel to gg_1

This shift can be resolved into a vertical component (RB_1) and a horizontal component (BR).

$$BR \; - \; BS \; = \; GZ \qquad BR \; = \; \frac{v \times hh_1}{V} \qquad BS \; = \; BG \sin \theta$$

Combining the above we get ATWOOD'S FORMULA for the moment of statical stability

$$\text{As } W \left(\frac{v \times hh_1}{V} \; - BG \sin \theta \right)$$

The vertical distance between G and B_1 is ZB_1 which is $RB_1 + RZ$.

$$RB_1 \; = \; \frac{v \times (gh + g_1h_1)}{V} \qquad RZ \; = \; BG \cos \theta$$

The vertical distance between B and G was BG before the vessel was heeled. Multiplying the difference between the vertical distance (i.e. the vertical separation of B and G) by the displacement, we have the dynamical stability, which from the above

$$\text{is } W \left(\frac{v \times (gh + g_1h_1)}{V} \; + BG \cos \theta \; - BG \right)$$

$$\text{or } W \left(\frac{v \times (gh + g_1h_1)}{V} \; - BG \text{ versine } \theta \right) \qquad \begin{array}{c} \text{this is known as} \\ \text{MOSELEY'S FORMULA} \end{array}$$

WALL SIDED STABILITY

If the ship's sides at the waterplane are parallel to one another (they are in most ships) and the deck edge is not immersed, the wedges of immersion and emersion may be considered as being symmetrical about the ship's centre line. In such cases the "wall sided formula" may be used to calculate the righting lever. This formula is shown on the following page and the calculation of the GZ using it is more straightforward than by Atwood's formula.

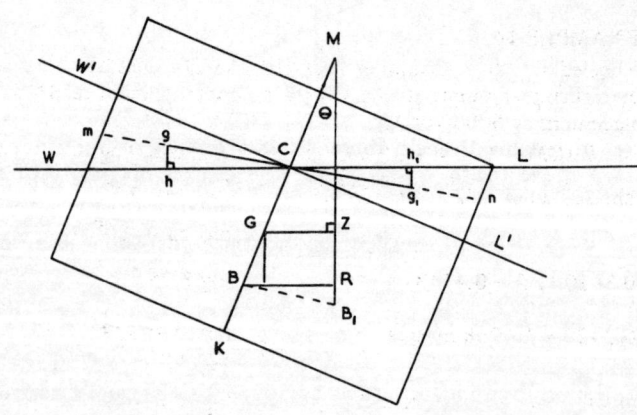

Let b   =   ½ breadth of ship

θ =   Angle of heel (a very small angle)

g, g_1 =   centres of gravity of immersed and emersed wedges

v   =   volume of either of the above wedges of unit length

then assuming n is midpoint of LL_1

nL_1 = $\dfrac{b}{2} \tan \theta$

Now v   = $½ b^2 \tan \theta$

BR   = $\dfrac{v \times hh_1}{V}$

hh_1 = $\dfrac{2}{3}$ projection of mn on line WL

    = $\dfrac{4}{3}$ of projection $CL' + L'n$ on WL

(Projection of Cn is the same as projection of $CL_1 + L_1n$ on WL)

hh_1 = $\dfrac{4}{3} (b \cos \theta + \dfrac{b}{2} \tan \theta \sin \theta)$

    = $\dfrac{4}{3} b \cos \theta (1 + ½ \tan^2 \theta)$

$v \times hh_1$ = $\dfrac{2}{3} b^3 \sin \theta (1 + ½ \tan^2 \theta)$

$\dfrac{v \times hh_1}{V}$ = $BM \sin \theta (1 + ½ \tan^2 \theta)$ =   BR

GZ   = $BR - BG \sin \theta$ and $BG = BM - GM$

    = $BM \sin \theta + (½ BM \tan^2 \theta \sin \theta) - (BM \sin \theta - GM \sin \theta)$

GZ   = $\sin \theta (GM + ½ BM \tan^2 \theta)$

WORKED EXAMPLE 16

A vessel is heeled to 20^0. Assuming that she is wall-sided at the draught concerned, calculate her righting moment if the GM is 1.2 metres and the BM is 7.5 metres. The vessel's displacement is 6000 tonnes.

GZ	=	$\sin \theta (GM + ½ BM \tan^2 \theta)$	By using logs
	=	$\sin 20^0 (1.2 + \dfrac{7.5}{2} \tan^2 20^0)$	log. tan 20^0 9.56107
			log. tan^2 20^0 $\dfrac{\times \quad 2}{9.12214}$
	=	$0.3420 (1.2 + 0.4968)$	log 3.75 0.57403
	=	0.3420×1.6968 metres	log. 0.49679 $\dfrac{}{9.69617}$
			+ 1.2
Righting Moment	=	W x GZ	log. 1.69679 0.22964
	=	$6000 \times 0.3420 \times 1.6968$	log. sin 20^0 9.53405
	=	3482 tonnes-metres	log. 6000 3.77815
			log. 3482 3.54184

THE EFFECT ON STABILITY caused by changing the relative positions of B, G and M.

In all cases the vessel shown upright is in equilibrium, but only in figures A and B is she in stable equilibrium.

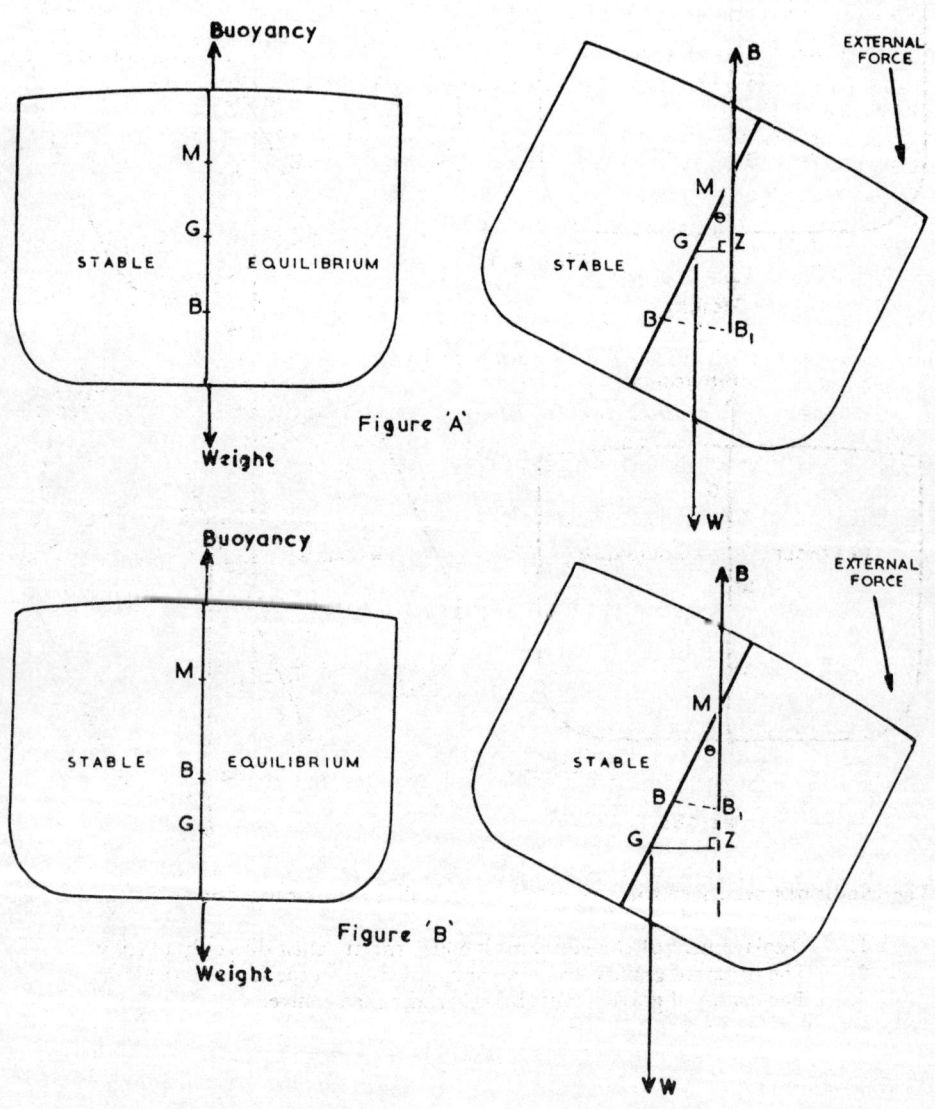

Figure 'A'

Figure 'B'

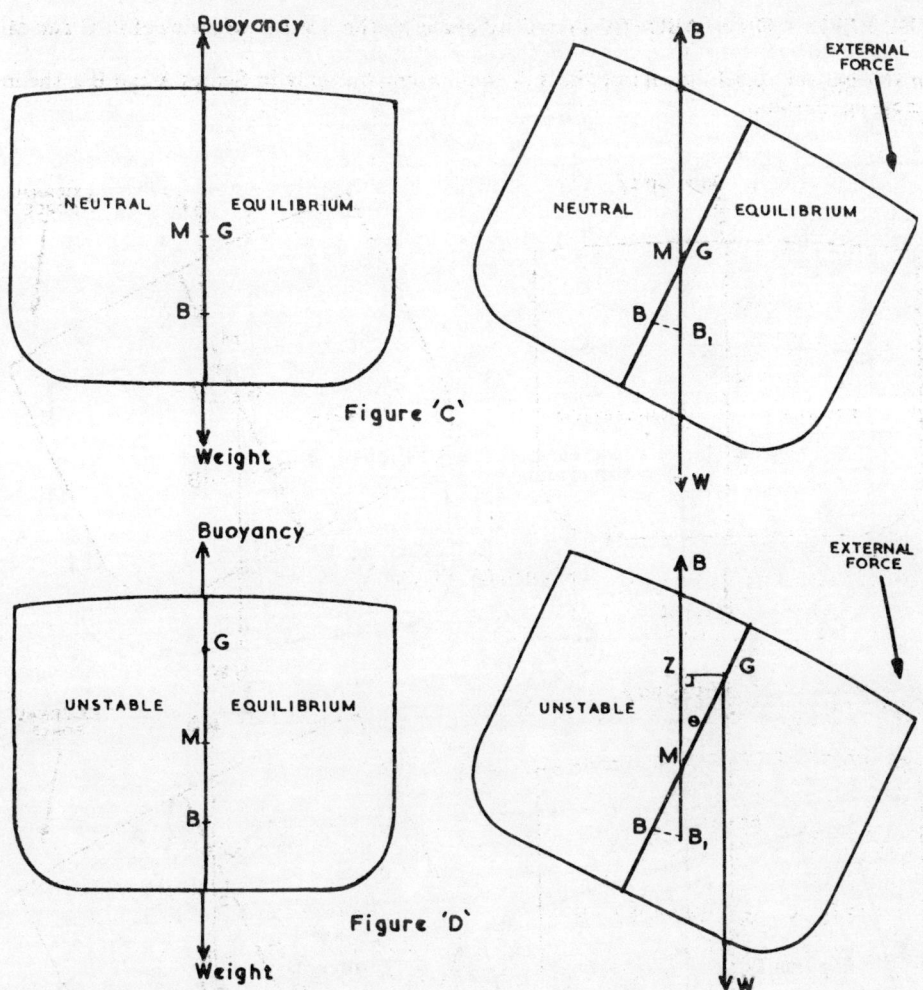

Figure 'C'

Figure 'D'

The conditions necessary for a vessel to be in stable equilibrium can be summarised as:-

1.   Displacement of the vessel must equal the upthrust due to buoyancy.
2.   The forces of gravity and buoyancy must be on the same vertical line.
3.   The centre of gravity must be below the metacentre.

Having seen that instability results when G rises above M, it may be thought that, under these circumstances, the vessel will capsize. Fortunately, this is not the case, as when the vessel starts to heel over, her breadth at the waterplane increases. This causes an increase in BM (BM = $\frac{I}{V}$, V remaining constant) which will eventually bring the metacentre above the centre of gravity. The angle at which the vessel comes to rest with positive stability is called the ANGLE OF LOLL. This is her new initial position and if further heeled she will return to this position. It should be noted that the metacentre is not on the centre line when the vessel is in the lolled position. Figures A, B, C, D, below illustrate the above text.

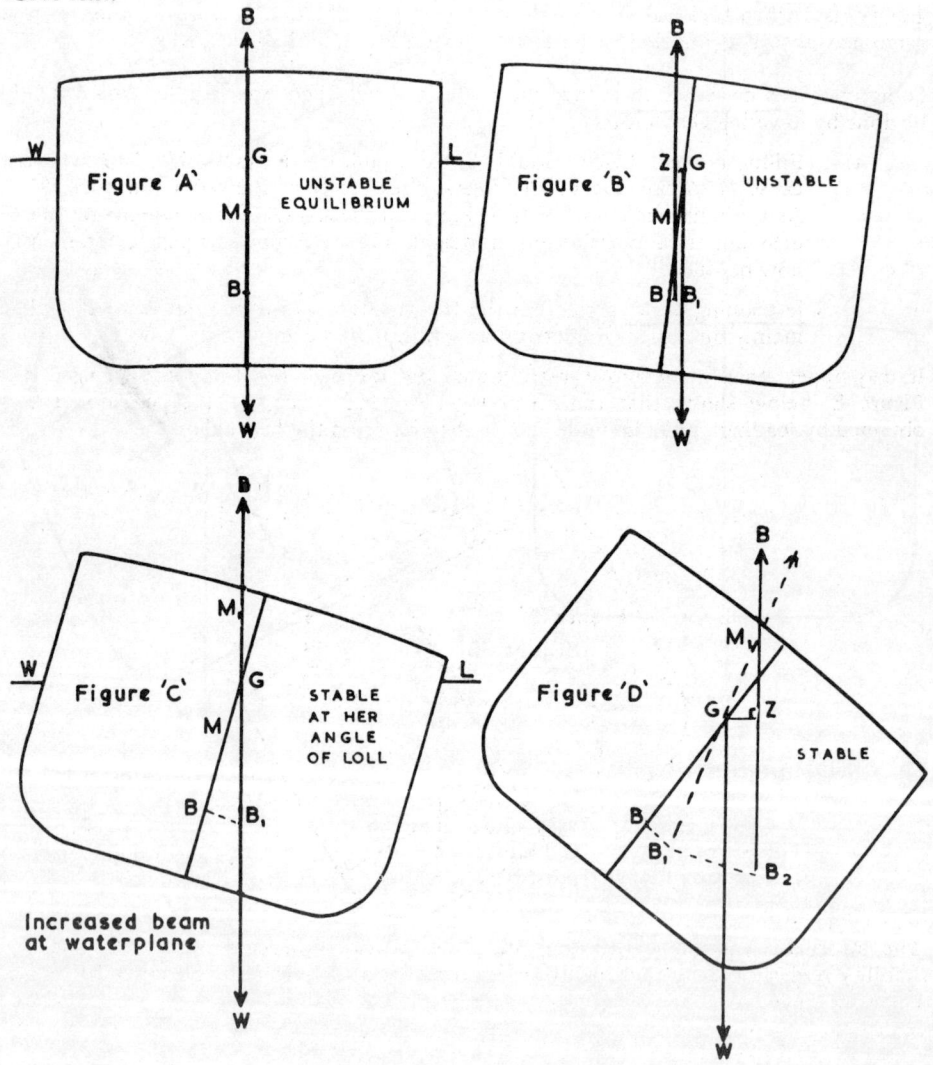

Using the "Wall sided" formula on page 49   and substituting zero for the GZ therein (i.e. the vessel is lolled) it can be shown that

$$\text{Tan angle of loll} = \sqrt{\frac{-2\,GM}{BM}}$$

$$\text{GM at angle of loll} = \frac{-2\,GM}{\cos.\ \text{angle of loll}}$$

the GM on the right hand side of each equation being the negative GM upright.

Vessels most prone to instability are those with deck cargoes of timber. The centre of gravity rises when fuel and water are consumed from the double bottom, and the deck cargo may absorb a considerable amount of water, if there is bad weather.

Sometimes it is necessary to reduce the angle to which the vessel is lolled, this can only be done by lowering G by either:-

a) Filling a small divided double bottom tank on the LOW side. This will first cause G to rise due to the free surface effect of the water (see page 93). As the tank becomes full G will fall and the residual list will be mainly due to unsymmetrical distribution of weight. The corresponding high side tank may now be filled.

or b) jettisoning deck cargo from the HIGH side. Again the residual list should be mainly due to unsymmetrical distribution of weight.

It may appear that in the above instructions, low and high should be interchanged, but Figure E. below shows that the greatest VERTICAL change in the position of G is obtained by loading on the low side and discharging from the high side.

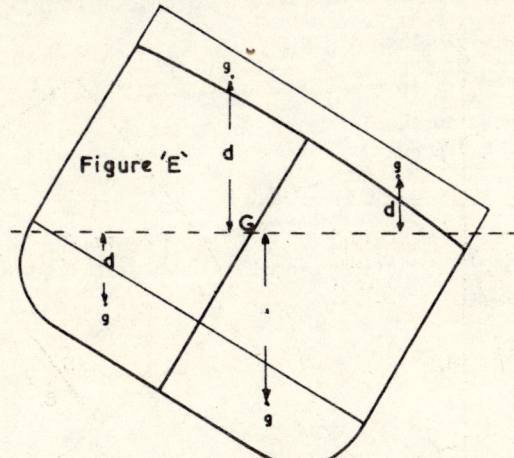

Figure 'E'

The information given on the foregoing pages provides the basic theory of transverse stability and should be thoroughly understood before passing to the practical, or calculation, aspect.

The theory of taking moments was explained on page 12. Several examples of taking them in a horizontal direction have already been given. They can be taken vertically in exactly the same manner as horizontally, the following text explains this.

TAKING MOMENTS ABOUT THE KEEL

(a)   Loading weights

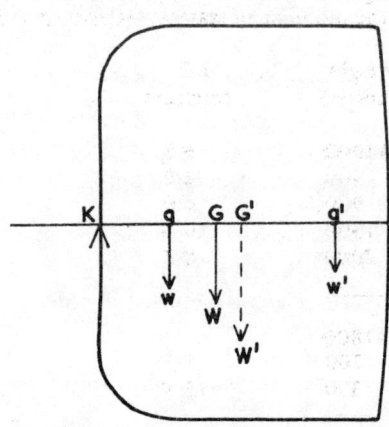

W' = $W + w + w'$
W is the weight of the ship
w, w' are weights loaded

$$KG' = \frac{\text{Sum of the moments about K}}{\text{Sum of the weights}} = \frac{(W \times KG) + (w \times Kg) + (w' \times Kg')}{W'}$$

(b)   Discharging weights

W' = $W - w - w'$
W is the weight of the ship
w, w' are weights discharged

$$KG' = \frac{\text{Sum of the moments about K}}{\text{Sum of the weights}} = \frac{(W \times KG) - (w \times Kg) - (w' \times Kg')}{W'}$$

It should be noted that the moment caused by the original displacement and KG of the vessel is always considered.

WORKED EXAMPLE 17

A vessel of 13,000 tonnes, KM 10.5m (assumed constant), KG 9.5m loads:- 400 tonnes KG 2.9m; 900 tonnes KG 6.0m; 1500 tonnes KG 10.6m; 2000 tonnes KG 8.3m. She discharges:- 700 tonnes KG 1.5m; 300 tonnes KG 12.7m.
Calculate the moment of statical stability if she is now heeled 8^0.

Weight (tonnes)	x	KG (metres)	=	Moment (tonnes-metres)
13000		9.5		123500
400		2.9		1160
900		6.0		5400
1500		10.6		15900
2000		8.3		16600
17800				162560
- 700		1.5		- 1050
- 300		12.7		- 3810
sum of weights 16800			sum of moments	157700

$$\text{New KG} = \frac{\text{sum of moments}}{\text{sum of weights}} = \frac{157700}{16800} \frac{\text{tonnes-metres}}{\text{tonnes}}$$

$$= \quad 9.387 \quad \text{metres}$$

KM	10.5 metres
GM	1.113 metres

$$\text{moment of statical stability} = W \times GM \times \sin\theta$$

$$= 16800 \times 1.113 \times \sin 8^0$$

$$= 2602.4 \text{ tonnes-metres}$$

WORKED EXAMPLE 18

A vessel displacing 5800 tonnes KM 7.0m KG 6.0m has to load a quantity of deck cargo KG 11.0m. What is the maximum quantity that she can load so that her GM is not less than 0.75m.

Let w tonnes be the amount to load on deck,
Then taking moments about the keel.

Weight	x	KG	=	Moment
5800		6.0		34800
w		11.0		11w

sum of the weights	5800 + w tonnes		sum of the moments	34800 + 11w tonnes-mtrs

$$\begin{aligned} KM &= 7.00m \\ \text{new GM} &= 0.75m \\ \text{new KG} &= 6.25m \end{aligned}$$

$$\text{New KG} = \frac{\text{sum of moments}}{\text{sum of weights}}$$

$$6.25 = \frac{34800 + 11w}{5800 + w}$$

$$36250 + 6.25w = 34800 + 11w$$

$$4.75w = 1450$$

$$w = 305.26 \text{ tonnes}$$

TAKING MOMENTS ABOUT THE CENTRE OF GRAVITY

When dealing with horizontal movements of weight, it is usually convenient to take moments about the centre of gravity. We may also take moments about the centre of gravity when dealing with vertical movements of weight, but, unless there is only one weight involved, it is usually easier to take the moments about the keel.

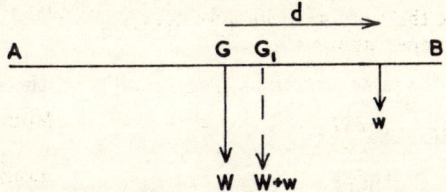

The bar AB represents a vessel of weight W tonnes acting through the centre of gravity G. Consider a weight of w tonnes loaded d metres from G. Take moments.

Weight	x	Distance	=	Moment
W		0		0
w		d		w x d
W + w				w x d

The distance of the new centre of gravity (G_1) from the point moments are taken (G). This is known as the shift of G or GG_1.

$$= \frac{\text{Sum of the moments}}{\text{Sum of the weights}}$$

i.e. GG_1

$$= \frac{w \times d}{W + w}$$

Similar expressions may be found for discharging and shifting weights, these are summarised below.

SHIFT OF G (GG_1)

When loading

$$GG_1 = \frac{w \times d}{W + w}$$ where   W is the vessel's displacement before loading the weight
w is the weight loaded
d is the distance of the loaded weight from the old centre of gravity

G always moves towards the loaded weights.

When discharging

$$GG_1 = \frac{w \times d}{W - w}$$ where   W is the vessel's displacement before discharging the weight
w is the weight discharged
d is the distance of the discharged weight from the old centre of gravity

G always moves away from the discharged weights.

When shifting

$$GG_1 = \frac{w \times d}{W}$$

where   W is the vessel's displacement
(this includes the weight shifted)
w is the weight shifted
d is the distance that the weight is shifted.

G always moves in the same direction as, and parallel to, the shifted weight.

WORKED EXAMPLE 18a

The previous example will now be re-worked taking our moments about G

KG deck	11.0m		KM	7.00m
KG ship	6.0m		KG	6.00m
d	5.0m		GM now	1.00m
			GM required	0.75m
			GG_1	0.25m upwards

Let w tonnes be the amount to load on deck

$$GG_1 = \frac{w \times d}{W + w}$$

$$0.25 = \frac{w \times 5}{5800 + w}$$

$$1450 + 0.25w = 5w$$

$$w = \frac{1450}{4.75}$$

$$w = 305.26 \text{ tonnes}$$

Let us now consider the effect on stability when a weight is loaded off the centre line.

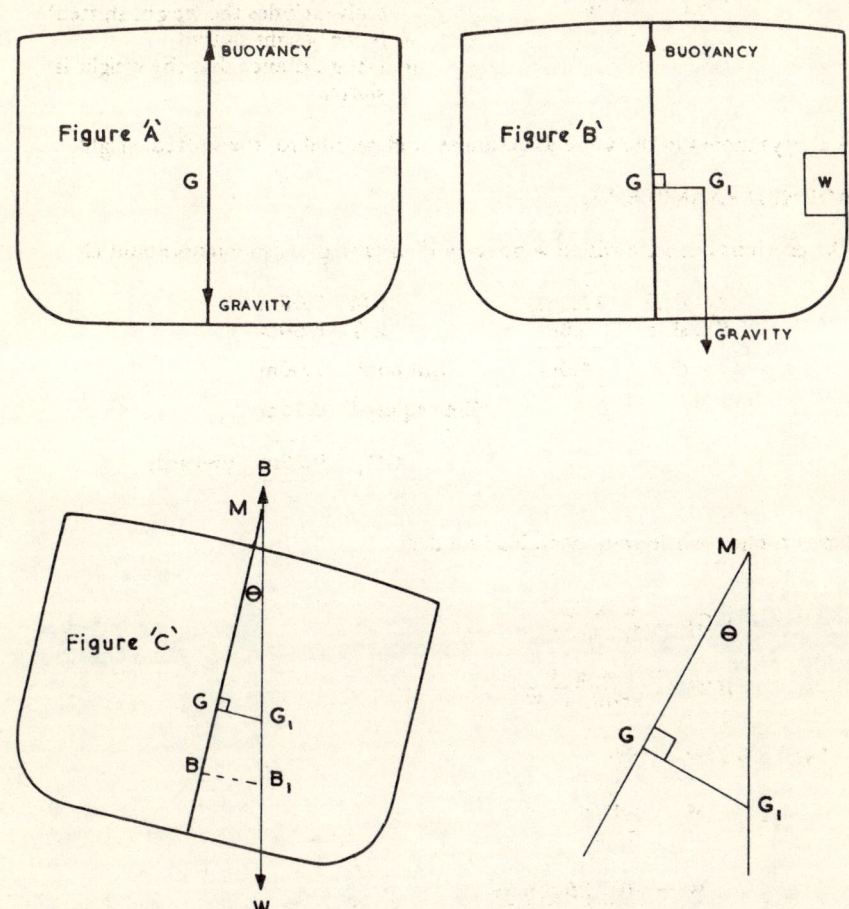

In figure A above, the forces of gravity and buoyancy are on the same vertical line. In figure B, G has moved to G_1 as the weight w has been loaded, this means that the forces of gravity and buoyancy are no longer on the same vertical line, in fact they are causing an upsetting couple. This couple forces the vessel to the position shown in figure C when forces B and W are again on the same vertical line. The vessel is now in equilibrium and this is her initial position

$$GG_1 \quad = \quad GM \tan \theta$$

Also

When loading, discharging or shifting weights away from the centre line, the shift of G caused should always be resolved into a vertical component and a horizontal component, so that there is a right angle at the ship's centre line.

WORKED EXAMPLE 19

A vessel of 6500 tonnes displacement has a KM 7.2m and KG 6.8m. A weight of 100 tonnes is shifted 2.3m to port and 3.9m upwards. If the vessel is initially upright, calculate the resulting list.

$$GG_1 \quad = \quad \frac{w \times d}{W}$$

for vertical shift

$$GG_1 = \frac{100 \times 3.9}{6500}$$

$$= \quad 0.06\text{m rise}$$

KG	6.8 m
KG_1	6.86m
KM	7.2 m
G_1M	0.34m

for horizontal shift

$$GG_1 \quad = \quad \frac{100 \times 2.3}{6500}$$

$$= \quad 0.0354\text{m to port}$$

$$\text{Tan } \theta \quad = \quad \frac{GG_1}{GM}$$

$$= \quad \frac{0.0354}{0.34}$$

$$\theta \quad = \quad 5° \ 56.7' \text{ to port}$$

WORKED EXAMPLE 20

A vessel of 7800 tonnes displacement KM 6.8m KG 6.0m, measured on the centre line, is listed 4° to starboard. 400 tonnes of cargo is to be loaded into the 'tween deck KG 6.0m. There is space 5.5m to port and 3.0m to starboard of the centre line. How much cargo should be loaded into each space in order that the vessel will be upright on completion?

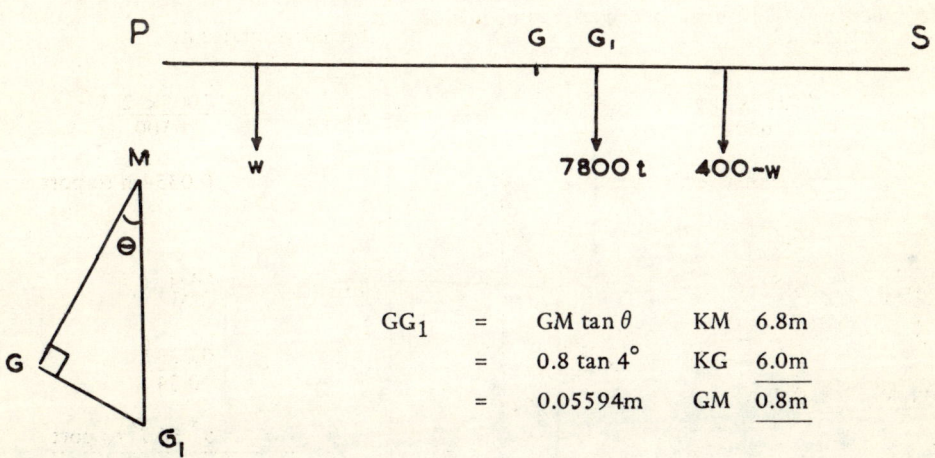

$$GG_1 = GM \tan \theta$$
$$= 0.8 \tan 4°$$
$$= 0.05594m$$

KM	6.8m
KG	6.0m
GM	0.8m

Let w tonnes be loaded on the port side, then (400 - w) tonnes will be loaded on the starboard side. For the vessel to be upright, the moments each side of the centre line will have to be equal.

i.e. $5.5w = (7800 \times 0.05594) + 3(400 - w)$

          $5.5w = 436.33 + 1200 - 3w$

          $w = \dfrac{1636.33}{8.5} = 192.5$ tonnes

i.e.   192.5 tonnes should be loaded on the port side
          207.5   ”   ”   ”   ”   ”   ” starboard side.

When working examples of this kind, a rough figure will always help the student to see what has to be done. Weights loaded should always be indicated by arrows pointing downwards and weights discharged by arrows pointing upwards.

PRINCIPLE OF SUSPENDED WEIGHTS

When a weight is suspended by a ship's derrick, its centre of gravity is to be considered as being at the derrick head, and it will remain at the derrick head as long as the weight is suspended. In other words it does not matter if the weight is 1cm or 10 metres above the deck, its C of G is still be be considered at the derrick head.

WORKED EXAMPLE 21

A vessel of 9920 tonnes displacement, KM 7.8m is to load two 40 tonne lifts on deck KG 13.5m and 5.5m each side of the centre line, by means of her heavy lift derrick whose head is 21.0m above the keel and maximum swing out 15m from the centre line. What should be the vessel's maximum KG before loading, if the list during loading is not to exceed 5°? (The inboard weight is to be loaded first.)

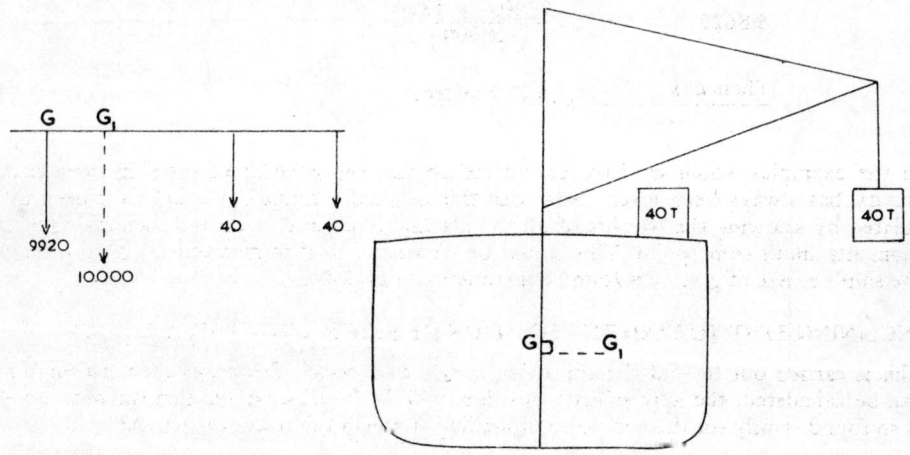

To find the horizontal shift of G.

Take moments about the centre line when the maximum list occurs.

Weight	x	Distance	=	Moment
9920		0		0
40		5.5		220
40		15.0		600
10000 tonnes				820 tonnes-metres

$$GG_1 = \frac{\text{Sum of the moments}}{\text{Sum of the weights}} = \frac{820}{10000} = 0.082m$$

$$
\begin{aligned}
GM &= GG_1 \cot \theta \\
&= 0.082 \cot 5° \\
&= 0.9373m
\end{aligned}
$$

$$KM = 7.800m$$

$$\text{Final KG} = 6.8627m$$

Let the original KG be x metres
Taking moments about the keel.

Weight	x	KG	=	Moment
9920		x		9920x
40		13.5		540
40		21.0		840
10000 tonnes				9920x + 1380 tonnes-metres

$$\text{Final KG} = \frac{\text{Sum of the moments}}{\text{Sum of the weights}}$$

$$6.8627 = \frac{9920x + 1380}{10000}$$

$$\text{Thence } x = 6.779 \text{ metres}$$

In the examples which we have considered so far, the position of the ship's centre of gravity has always been given. How was this originally found? It could have been calculated by knowing the weights of all the plating, rivets and so on and then taking their moments about some point. This would be laborious, so that in practice the position of the ship's centre of gravity is found experimentally as under.

INCLINING TEST TO FIND THE POSITION OF SHIP'S CENTRE OF GRAVITY

This is carried out to find the approximate GM of a vessel, thence, as the position of M can be calculated, the approximate position of G. It should be noted that the position of G so found is only for the condition of loading at which the test is carried out.

When carrying out the test a plumbline is suspended from a hatch coaming on the middle-line down to the lower hold where a graduated batten is set up horizontally. A known weight (between $\frac{1}{500}$th and $\frac{1}{1000}$th of the vessel's displacement) is then shifted trans-versely a known distance, this causes the vessel to list and the plumbline to move across the batten. The deflection is measured. (In practice two or three plumblines are used and the inclination done several times, a mean deflection being used in the calculation). To ensure that the result of the test is reliable:-

1. There should be no wind, or if any, the vessel should be head to wind.

2. The moorings should be well slacked down (so that the vessel is clear of the quay).

3. Only those directly concerned with the test should be on board, and when the weights have been shifted (usually 25kg (56lb) weights are carried by hand) they should stand on the centre line.

4. Free surfaces of liquids should be kept to a minimum, this will save laborious calculations to correct the results.

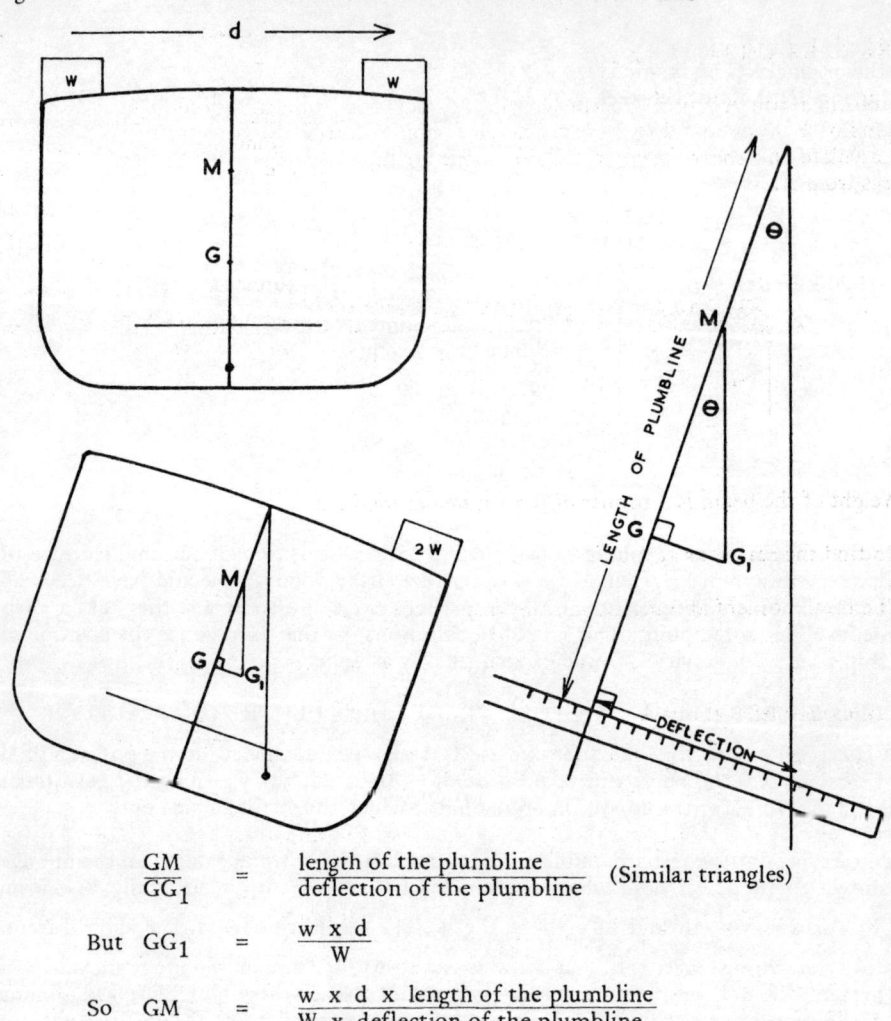

$$\frac{GM}{GG_1} = \frac{\text{length of the plumbline}}{\text{deflection of the plumbline}} \quad \text{(Similar triangles)}$$

$$\text{But} \quad GG_1 = \frac{w \times d}{W}$$

$$\text{So} \quad GM = \frac{w \times d \times \text{length of the plumbline}}{W \times \text{deflection of the plumbline}}$$

WORKED EXAMPLE 22

When a vessel of 5300 tonnes displacement KM 7.7m is inclined by shifting 10 tonnes 16m, it is noted that the mean deflection of a plumbline 12m long is 33.25 cm. What is her KG?

$$GM = \frac{10 \times 16 \times 12 \times 100}{5300 \times 33.25}$$

$$= 1.09 \text{ m}$$

$$KM = 7.70 \text{ m}$$

$$KG = \underline{6.61 \text{ m}}$$

ROLLING

The reader will now be aware that the stability of the vessel depends on the righting moment which can be varied either by changing the GZ or the displacement. A change in either of these can also affect the rolling period of the ship and some notes on this follow.

WAVE PERIOD is the time in seconds between successive crests, or troughs, passing a fixed point.

APPARENT WAVE PERIOD is the time in seconds between successive crests or troughs, passing an observer on board ship.

SHIP'S PERIOD is the time in seconds taken by a vessel doing a complete roll (e.g. Port-Starboard - Port).

A dangerous state of affairs can arise if the ship's still water period and the apparent wave period are equal. This is known as SYNCHRONISM and, if allowed to continue, it could capsize a vessel.

It should be noted that the movement of a vessel when rolling is similar to that of a pendulum, this being so, an expression can be formed for the vessel's period when in still water as under.

$$\text{Still water period} \quad = \quad 2\pi \sqrt{\frac{k^2}{GM.g}}$$

where k is the radius of gyration. This can be increased by stowing weights well away from the ship's centre of gravity, g is acceleration due to gravity, GM in metres.

It can be seen that if the radius of gyration remains constant, the period can be altered by increasing or decreasing the GM. As the ship's period will normally be greater than the wave period, an increase in GM will bring the ship's period nearer to the wave period and possible synchronism. It would seem that a small GM is safer than a large GM. Certainly, a vessel's movement is easier and more comfortable when the GM is small, but she is "tender" and could possibly be made unstable should cargo or ballast shift. A vessel with a large GM is "stiff" and has an uncomfortable, jerky movement in a seaway. However, should cargo or ballast be liable to shift, a large GM is safer than a small GM.

What is a reasonable GM? Somewhere about 3% - 4% of the beam in cargo and passenger vessels and about 8% in a tanker should make for comfortable and safe vessels. Minimum stability requirements are given on page 97.

When loading, weights should be 'winged out' and not concentrated on the centreline. This also affects the ship's period, but not to the same extent as does the GM.

If it is found that a vessel is tending to synchronise, then the apparent wave period should be changed either by altering course or altering speed.

The onset of synchronism can be recognised by the increase in the angle to which the vessel is rolling. At each oscillation (half roll) this angle increases by about 1½ times the wave slope. It will be seen that this angle could soon reach dangerous limits in synchronous conditions.

The operation of stabilizers either gyro type or flume tank is beyond the present scope of this book.

EFFECT ON DRAUGHT CAUSED BY A VESSEL HEELING OR LISTING

To understand the implication of this, DRAUGHT must first be defined. It is the minimum depth of water that is necessary to float the ship, which is the distance from the waterline to the lowest point of the ship.

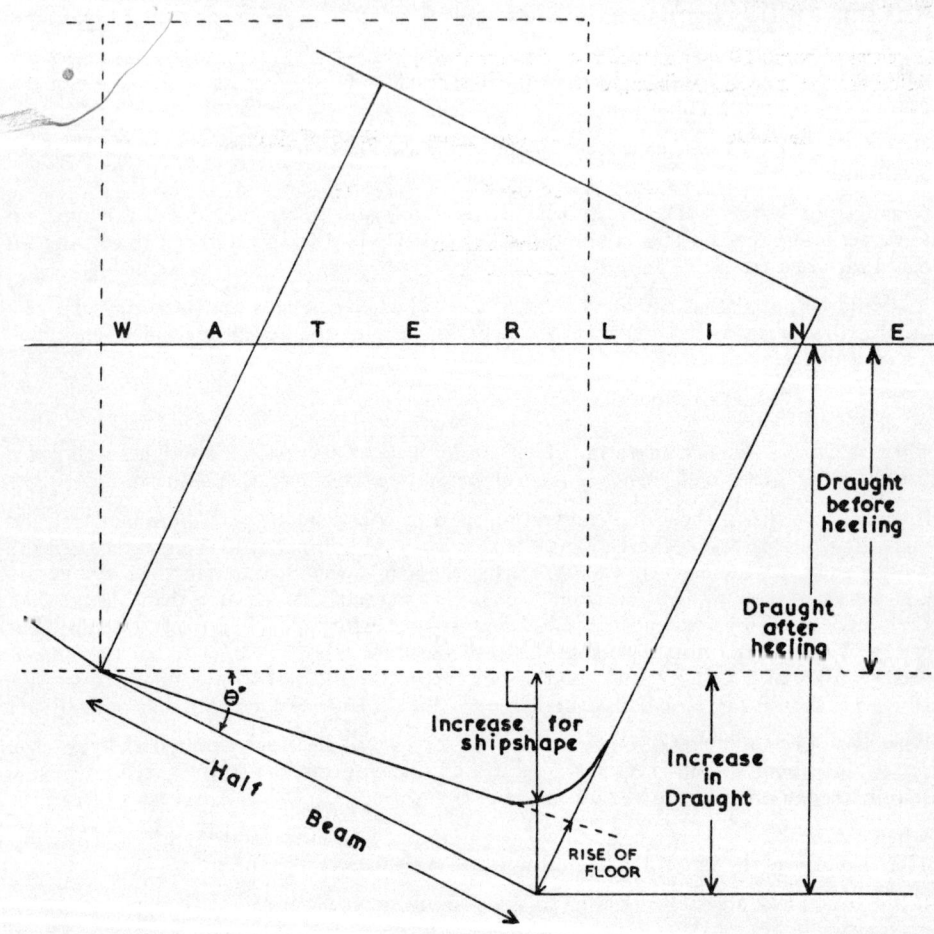

In the diagram, where for clarity only half of the ship is shown, it is assumed that the vessel will heel about the keel, this is not quite correct, but it gives an answer sufficiently close to the true answer for practical purposes. If the vessel is boxshaped the increase in draught is ½ beam sin θ.

When dealing with a shipshape, the rise of floor has to be considered. Although this is measured along the ship's side, for practical purposes the increase in the draught is assumed to be decreased by the rise of floor, this gives a slight safety margin.

It can now be seen that the increase of draught due to heel is equal to: ½ Beam sin θ - Rise of floor.

After about 3° or 4° heel the bilge keel will be the lowest point of the vessel and in shallow water is liable to damage if the vessel is not kept nearly upright.

WORKED EXAMPLE 23

A vessel of beam 20 metres and rise of floor 15cm is listed 4°.
Calculate the increase in draught.

Increase	=	½ Beam sin θ - Rise of floor
	=	10 sin 4° - 0.15
	=	0.548 metres

CHAPTER FIVE

Longitudinal Stability

TRIM is the difference between the draught at the forward perpendicular and the draught at the after perpendicular.

CHANGE OF TRIM is the difference between the original trim and the final trim.

CENTRE OF FLOTATION (C.F.) OR TIPPING CENTRE (T.C.) is the geometrical centre of the waterplane and the point about which the vessel trims.

The change of draught due to a change of trim must not be confused with the change of trim.

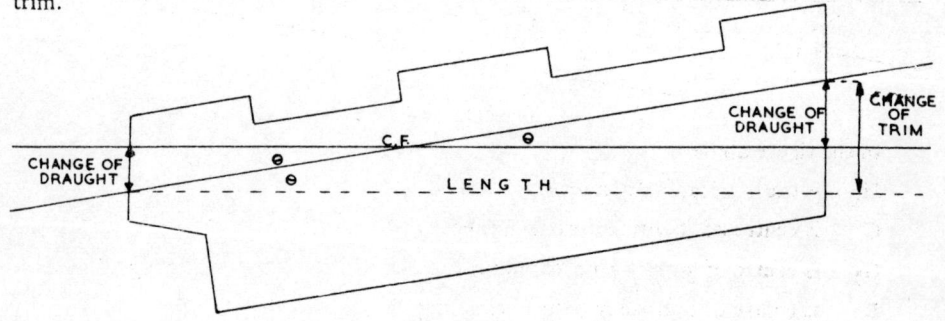

In the diagram above θ is the angle of trim

It can be seen that $\text{Tan } \theta = \dfrac{\text{The change of trim}}{\text{The length of the vessel}}$

$\text{Tan } \theta = \dfrac{\text{The change of draught forward}}{\text{The distance of the forward perpendicular from the centre of flotation}}$

$\text{Tan } \theta = \dfrac{\text{The change of draught aft}}{\text{The distance of the after perpendicular from the centre of flotation}}$

It follows (by transposing the above formulae) that the change of draught at a perpendicular due to a change of trim

$= \dfrac{\text{The distance of that perpendicular from the centre of flotation}}{\text{The length of the vessel}} \quad x \quad \text{Change of trim}$

TO FIND THE MOMENT TO CHANGE TRIM ONE CENTIMETRE (MCT 1 cm) which is the moment required to change the trim by one centimetre. This is important.

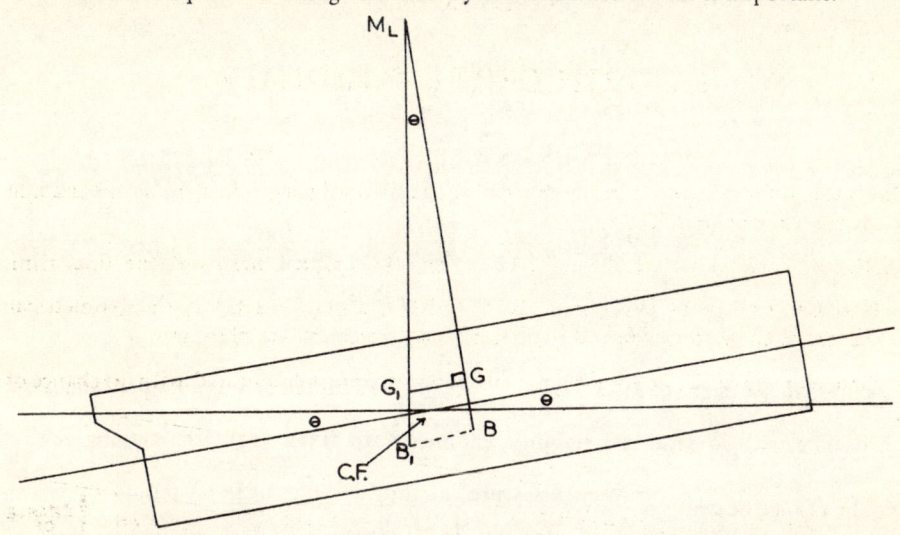

In the figure above

M_L is the longitudinal metacentre

G   is centre of gravity before trimming

G_1 is centre of gravity after trimming

B   is centre of buoyancy before trimming

B_1 is centre of buoyancy after trimming

θ is the angle of trim

Now $\dfrac{GG_1}{GM_L}$ $=$ Tan θ $=$ $\dfrac{\text{Change of trim}}{\text{Length of the vessel}}$

$\qquad GG_1 \qquad = \qquad \dfrac{GM_L \times \text{change of trim}}{\text{Length of vessel}}$

$\qquad GG_1 \qquad = \qquad \dfrac{GM_L}{100L}$ (if change of trim is 1 cm: $1\,\text{cm} = \dfrac{1}{100}\text{m}$)

or $\quad \dfrac{w \times d}{W} \qquad = \qquad \dfrac{GM_L}{100L}$ (as $GG_1 = \dfrac{w \times d}{W}$ and w x d is moment in tonnes-metres W is displacement in tonnes)

or $\quad w \times d \qquad = \qquad \dfrac{W \times GM_L}{100L}$

but w x d is the moment which has changed the trim one centimetre.

$\therefore \quad$ MCT 1 cm $\quad = \quad \dfrac{W \times GM_L}{100L}$ tonnes-metres (t-m)

APPROXIMATION OF MCT 1cm FOR A BOX-SHAPED VESSEL

$$\text{MCT 1cm} = \frac{W \times GM_L}{100L}$$

$$\text{as } GM_L \doteqdot BM_L \quad \text{then} \quad GM_L \doteqdot \frac{L^2}{12d}$$

$$\text{MCT 1cm} \doteqdot \frac{1.025 \times L \times B \times d \times L^2}{100 \times L \times 12d} = \frac{1.025 \, LB}{100} \times \frac{L}{12}$$

$$= \frac{1.025 \, T}{1.025} \times \frac{L}{12} = T \times \frac{100T}{12 \times 1.025 \, B} \quad \text{where} \quad T = TPC$$

$$= \frac{100 \, T^2}{12.3 \, B} \doteqdot \frac{8T^2}{B}$$

For a ship shape, a figure of MCT 1cm $\doteqdot \frac{7T^2}{B}$ might be adopted as a useful approximation.

When dealing with longitudinal stability, moments are taken about the tipping centre and

$$\text{The change of trim} = \frac{\text{Moments caused about the centre of flotation}}{\text{MCT 1cm}}$$

When loading or discharging a weight

The moment caused = The weight loaded or discharged x its distance from the centre of flotation.

When shifting a weight

The moment caused = The weight shifted x the distance it is shifted.

It must be remembered that when weights are loaded or discharged there will be an increase or decrease in the vessel's mean draught, or to be more precise, the draught at the tipping centre. Students may find it more convenient to consider all the weights to be loaded at the tipping centre and then shifted to their correct positions. All the weights to be discharged may be considered to have been shifted to the tipping centre and then taken out.

When the MCT 1cm is given, it should be considered a constant for that question. When the MCT 1cm has to be calculated, the displacement given before loading or discharging weights is generally used, although to be exact the mean displacement should be used. Great care must be taken when applying change of trim and sinkage or rise, which are in centimetres, to the draughts which are usually in metres. Ensure that all are in the same units.

Occasionally the position of the centre of flotation is not given, in such cases it should always be assumed to be at midlength.

When attempting trim problems, a rough sketch will help the student, who should always indicate weights loaded by arrows pointing downward and weights discharged by arrows pointing upward. The arrows will now indicate the direction of rotation of the vessel about the tipping centre caused by loading or discharging the various weights.

WORKED EXAMPLE 24

A weight of 54 tonnes is shifted from No.1 to No.2, a distance of 20metres, on a vessel MCT 1cm 120 tonnes-metres. Calculate the change of trim.

Change of trim   = $\dfrac{\text{Moment being caused}}{\text{MCT 1cm}}$

                   = $\dfrac{54 \times 20}{120}$ A ←——————— F

                   =   9 cm by the stern.

N.B. The positions of Nos. 1 and 2 relative to the centre of flotation are immaterial. The distance and direction the weight is shifted are the important factors.

WORKED EXAMPLE 25

A vessel 120m long MCT 1cm 100 tonnes-metres, TPC 25 is drawing 6.00m F 6.60m A. A weight of 250 tonnes is loaded 12m forward of the centre of flotation which is 2m abaft midlength. Calculate the new draughts forward and aft.

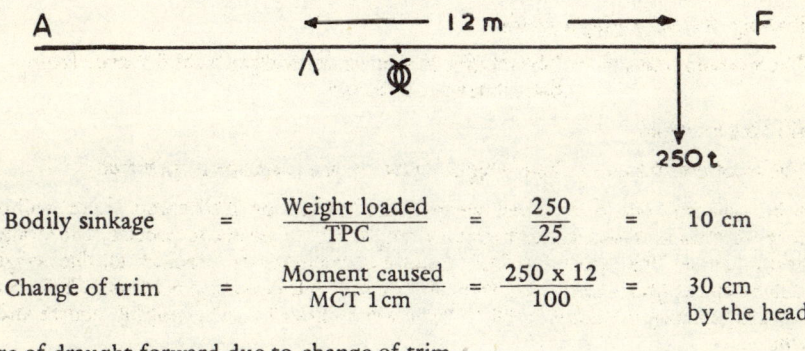

Bodily sinkage   = $\dfrac{\text{Weight loaded}}{\text{TPC}}$ = $\dfrac{250}{25}$ =   10 cm

Change of trim   = $\dfrac{\text{Moment caused}}{\text{MCT 1cm}}$ = $\dfrac{250 \times 12}{100}$ =   30 cm by the head

Change of draught forward due to change of trim

                   = $\dfrac{62}{120}$ x   30   =   15.5cm increase

Change of draught aft due to change of trim

                   = $\dfrac{58}{120}$ x   30   =   14.5cm decrease

		F	A
Original draught		6.000	6.600
Sinkage		.100	.100
		6.100	6.700
Change due to trim	+	.155	− .145
Final draughts		6.255m	6.555 m

WORKED EXAMPLE 26

A vessel of 6600 tonnes displacement 120m in length, GM_L 140m is drawing 4.8m F 4.5m A. The centre of flotation is 2m abaft midlength. How much cargo should be discharged from No.2. which is 16m forward of amidships, so that the vessel would be trimmed 15cm by the stern?

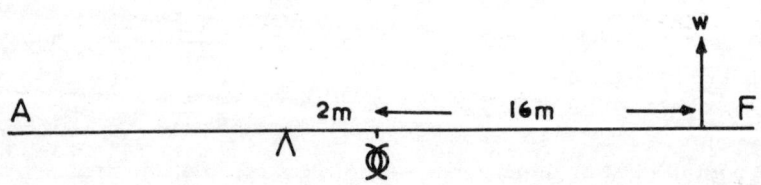

Let w tonnes be the weight to discharge from No.2. This will cause a moment of 18w tonnes-metres about the centre of flotation.

Present draughts	4.80m F 4.50m A	MCT 1cm	$= \dfrac{W \times GM_L}{100L}$
Present trim	0.30m by the head		$= \dfrac{6600 \times 140}{100 \times 120}$
Required trim	0.15m by the stern		
Change of trim required	0.45m by the stern		= 77 tonnes-metres

The moment required to cause the above change of trim is 45 x 77 tonnes-metres.

The moment caused   =   The moment required

18w   =   45 x 77

w   =   192.50 tonnes

WORKED EXAMPLE 27

A vessel 150m in length, 18m in breadth, MCT 1cm 150 tonnes-metres, TPC 25 is drawing 6.35m F 6.65m A and loads the following:-

230 tonnes in No.1.   50m forward of the centre of flotation
800   ”   ” No.3.   20m ”   ”   ”   ”   ”   ”
500   ”   ” No.4.   21m abaft   ”   ”   ”   ”   ”

She discharges 200 tonnes from No.2.   36m forward of the centre of flotation
  ”   ”   105   ”   ” F.P. tank   60m ”   ”   ”   ”   ”   ”

The centre of flotation is 5m abaft midlength. Calculate the new draughts.

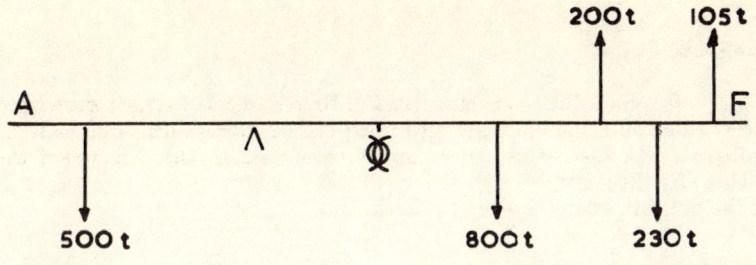

Weight x	Distance from C.F.	=	Moment in tonnes-metres	
			Forward	Aft
230	50 F		11500	-
800	20 F		16000	-
500	21 A		-	10500
- 200	36 F		-	7200
- 105	60 F		-	6300

Net
weight 1225 tonnes
loaded

27500   24000

$$\text{Resultant Moment} = \frac{27500}{24000} \quad 3500 \text{ tonnes-metres forward}$$

$$\text{Sinkage} = \frac{\text{Weight loaded}}{\text{TPC}} \qquad \text{Change of trim} = \frac{\text{Resultant Moment}}{\text{MCT 1cm}}$$

$$= \frac{1225}{25} \qquad\qquad = \frac{3500}{150}$$

$$= 49 \text{ cm} \qquad\qquad = 23.33 \text{ cm by the head}$$

$$\text{Change of draught forward due to change of trim} = \frac{80}{150} \times 23.33$$

$$= 12.44 \text{ cm increase}$$

$$\text{Change of draught aft due to change of trim} = \frac{70}{150} \times 23.33$$

$$= 10.89 \text{ cm decrease}$$

	F	A
Old draughts	6.350m	6.650m
Sinkage	0.490m	0.490m
Change of draught due to change of trim	+ 0.124m	- 0.109m
New draught	6.964m	7.031m

WORKED EXAMPLE 28

A vessel of 9000 tonnes displacement, length 120m, GM_L 160m is trimmed 8cm by the head. After loading 300 tonnes 24 metres forward of the midlength, 400 tonnes 30 metres abaft midlength and discharging 200 tonnes from midlength, it is noted that she is trimmed 18cm by the stern.
Calculate the position of the centre of flotation.

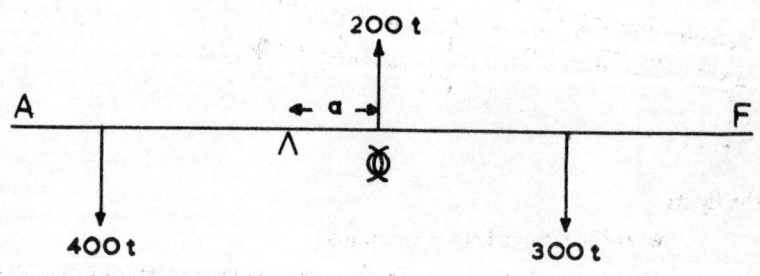

MCT 1cm	$= \dfrac{W \times GM_L}{100L}$	Original trim	=	8cm by the head
		Final trim	=	18cm by the stern
	$= \dfrac{9000 \times 160}{100 \times 120}$	Change of trim	=	26cm by the stern
	$=$ 120 tonnes-metres			

Let us assume that the centre of flotation is 'a' metres abaft midlength.
Then taking moments about the centre of flotation

The moment caused by loading and discharging	=	The moment required to change the trim 26cm.
400 (30 - a) + 200a - 300 (24 + a)	=	120 x 26
12000 - 400a + 200a - 7200 - 300a	=	3120
500a	=	1680
a	=	3.36 metres

The centre of flotation is 3.36m abaft midlength.

If the assumption, that the centre of flotation was abaft midlength, had been incorrect, the result would have been a negative quantity. This would indicate that the centre of flotation was the opposite side of midlength to that which it had been assumed.

TO FIND WHERE TO PLACE A WEIGHT TO KEEP THE DRAUGHT CONSTANT AT ONE OF THE PERPENDICULARS.

Assuming that the draught aft is to be kept constant.

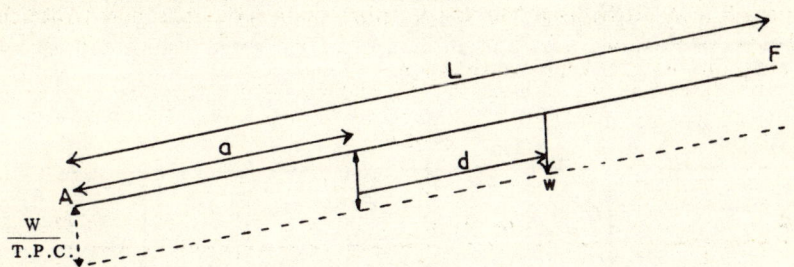

Then in the figure

> w is the weight loaded in tonnes.
>
> d is the distance in metres from the centre of flotation that the weight is to be loaded.
>
> a is the distance in metres of the after perpendicular from the centre of flotation.
>
> L is the length of the vessel in metres.

If w is loaded at the centre of flotation, the loading sinkage will be $\dfrac{w}{TPC}$ For the draught aft to remain constant, a change of draught equal to the sinkage will have to be caused, this will be caused by shifting w tonnes d metres.

$$\text{Then} \quad \frac{w \times d \times a}{MCT\,1cm \times L} \quad = \quad \frac{w}{TPC}$$

$$\text{Thence } d \quad = \quad \frac{MCT\,1cm \times L}{TPC \times a}$$

Note: This formula will only hold good if the hydrostatic data does not change.

WORKED EXAMPLE 29

A vessel 150m in length, MCT 1cm 140 tonnes-metres TPC 20, centre of flotation 5m abaft midlength, is loading at a certain port. It is noted that she reaches her required draught aft when there are still several tonnes of cargo on the quay.
Where should the cargo be loaded in one block so as to maintain the correct draught aft?

$$d \quad = \quad \frac{MCT\,1cm \times L}{TPC \times a}$$

$$= \quad \frac{140 \times 150}{20 \times 70}$$

$$= \quad 15 \text{ metres forward of the centre of flotation}$$

WORKED EXAMPLE 30

A vessel drawing 6.75m forward 7.75m aft MCT 1cm 140 tonnes-metres, TPC 15 has cargo space available in Nos. 2 and 4 holds, 50m forward and 40m abaft the centre of flotation which is at midlength. How much cargo should be loaded in each hold if the ship is to complete loading with a mean draught of 8.0m and trimmed 15 cm by the stern?

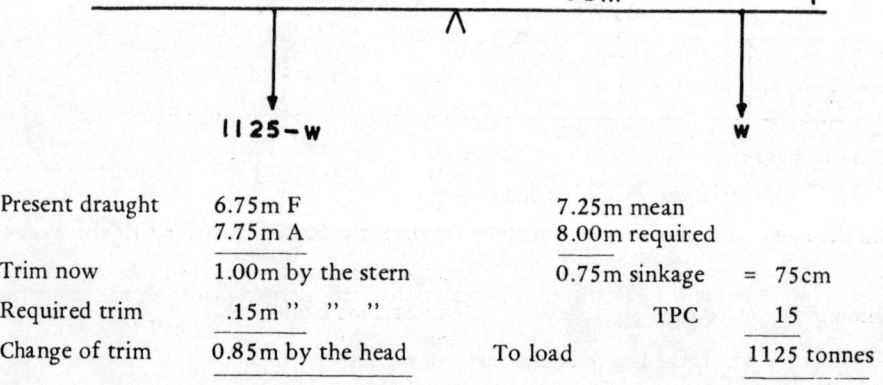

Present draught	6.75m F	7.25m mean	
	7.75m A	8.00m required	
Trim now	1.00m by the stern	0.75m sinkage	= 75cm
Required trim	.15m " " "	TPC	15
Change of trim	0.85m by the head	To load	1125 tonnes

Let w tonnes be loaded in No. 2.

Then (1125 - w) tonnes will be loaded in No.4.

Now the Resultant Moment   =   The moment to be caused

Forward		Aft		Forward
50w	-	40 (1125 - w)	=	85 x 140
50w	- 45000	+ 40w	=	11900
		90w	=	56900
		w	=	632.22 tonnes in No. 2.
			and	492.78 tonnes in No. 4.

WORKED EXAMPLE 31

A vessel MCT 1cm 150 tonnes-metres TPC 20 is drawing 8.4m F 9.0m A. She is to discharge 765 tonnes of cargo of which 425 tonnes is discharged from No.3. hold, the C.G. of which is 6.5m abaft the centre of flotation. How much should be discharged from Nos. 1 and 5 holds, 50m forward and 40m abaft the centre of flotation respectively to complete discharging on an even keel?

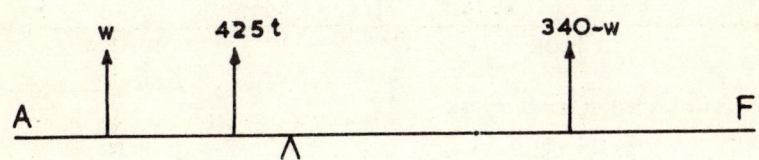

Present draught	8.40m F	Total to discharge	765 T.
	9.00m A	Already discharged	425 T.
Trim now	0.60m by the stern	To discharge from Nos. 1 and 5	340 T.
Required	0		
Change of trim	0.60m by the head		

Let w tonnes be discharged from No. 5

Then (340 - w) tonnes will be discharged from No. 1.

Now: The resultant moment   =   The moment to be caused

Forward		Forward		Aft			Forward
40w	+	(425 x 6.5)	-	50 (340 - w)	=		60 x 150
40w	+	2762.5	-	17000 + 50w	=		9000
				90w	=		23237.5
				w	=		258.2 tonnes from No.5.
						and	81.8 tonnes from No.1.

It will be noted that in the two previous examples w tonnes are loaded at or discharged from the end where the GREATER MOMENT is to be caused. Students will probably find it convenient to do likewise, although so long as the smaller moment is taken from the greater moment it really does not matter at which end w is placed.

WORKED EXAMPLE 32

A vessel of 5080 tonnes light displacement is at present floating at a mean draught of 7m and is trimmed 60 cm by the stern, her deadweight being 5720 tonnes. Her length is 150m, GM_L 200m, TPC 25. In order to pass over a bar her after draught is not to exceed 7.2m. Calculate the minimum amount of water to put in the forepeak tank 60m forward of the centre of flotation (which is amidships) to achieve the required draught.

$$\text{MCT 1cm} \quad = \quad \frac{W \times GM_L}{100L} \quad = \quad \frac{10800 \times 200}{100 \times 150} \quad = \quad 144 \text{ tonnes-metres}$$

Let w tonnes be loaded in the forepeak

This will cause a bodily sinkage of $\frac{w}{25}$ cm

and change of trim of $\frac{60w}{144}$ cm

giving a change of draught aft of $\frac{60w}{144 \times 2}$ (as CF is at midlength)

Mean draught	=	7.00 m
½ present trim	=	.30 m
Present draught aft	=	7.30 m
Sinkage	=	$\frac{w}{2500}$ m
		$7.3 + \frac{w}{2500}$ m
Required draught	=	7.2 m
Change required	=	$0.1 + \frac{w}{2500}$ m

Change required	=	Change caused
$10 + \frac{w}{25}$ cm	=	$\frac{60w}{288}$ cm
$\frac{5w}{24} - \frac{w}{25}$	=	10
w	=	59.406 tonnes

Another method by which the above type of problem can be solved is shown in the next example.

WORKED EXAMPLE 33

A vessel length 120m, MCT 1cm 120 tonnes-metres, TPC 15 is drawing 6.8m F, 7.1m A. It is required to bring the after draught to 6.8m by pumping out water from the after peak tank whose centre of gravity is 50m abaft the CF which is 4m abaft mid-length. What is the minimum quantity of water to be discharged?

Let y cm be the bodily rise when the water is discharged.

The amount of water pumped out will be 15y tonnes.

Draught aft	=	7.10 m	or	710 cm
Bodily rise	=			y cm
				(710-y) cm
Required draught				680 cm
Change required				(30 - y)cm

Change of trim to be caused is $(30-y) \dfrac{120}{56}$

This requires a moment of $(30-y) \dfrac{120}{56} \times 120$ tonnes-metres.

The moment caused by discharging from A.P. is $15y \times 50$ tonnes-metres.

Then $15y \times 50$	=	$(30-y)\dfrac{120}{56} \times 120$
Whence y	=	7.659
Water to pump out	=	15y
	=	114.885 tonnes.

TRUE MEAN DRAUGHT

The draught at the centre of flotation is the true mean draught and this does not change if the vessel is trimmed by shifting weights fore and aft. The mean draught which is the draught at midlength changes with trim unless the centre of flotation is at midlength. There is a correction to apply to the apparent mean draught in order to obtain the true mean draught and this is illustrated in the next example. The correction is sometimes known as the correction for layer.

WORKED EXAMPLE 34

A vessel whose length is 150m, TPC 20 is drawing 6.8m F 8.0m A. Her centre of flotation is 5m abaft mid-length. How much cargo can be loaded if she is to complete on an even keel at a draught of 7.70m?

Present draughts   6.80 m)
                      8.00 m) Mean 7.40 m

Trim   1.20 m by the stern

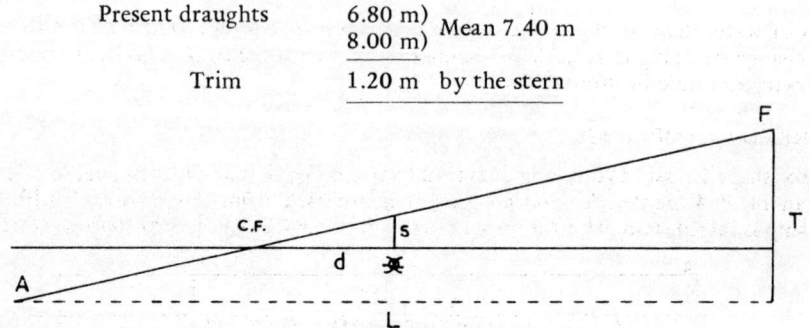

Let s be the difference in cm between the mean draught and the draught at the centre of flotation. This latter draught is the true mean draught.

d   =   distance of centre of flotation abaft mid-length

T   =   trim in cm

L   =   length of vessel in metres.

$$\frac{s}{d} = \frac{T}{L} \quad \text{and} \quad s = \frac{T \times d}{L} = \frac{120 \times 5}{150} = 4\text{cm}$$

Mean	7.40 m
Correction +	0.04 m
True mean	7.44 m
required	7.70 m
Sinkage	0.26 m or 26 cm
TPC	20
To load	520 tonnes

BILGING AN END COMPARTMENT

The effects of bilging a midship compartment were considered in worked examples 3 and 4. If an end compartment is bilged there will still be a loss of buoyancy and therefore a sinkage. The loss of buoyancy at the end of a vessel causes a shift of the centre of buoyancy away from the end and this shift is the trimming lever on which the total buoyancy acts to cause a trimming moment and therefore a change of trim.

Loss of waterplane at the end also causes a movement of the centre of flotation so that the change of draught at each perpendicular due to the change of trim is not equal. The following example illustrates this.

WORKED EXAMPLE 35

A box shaped vessel 170m long and 15m beam, is floating on an even keel in salt water at a draught of 4 metres. An end compartment forward, 10m long and the full breadth of the ship is bilged. Calculate the new draughts if the MCT 1cm is 100 tonnes-metres.

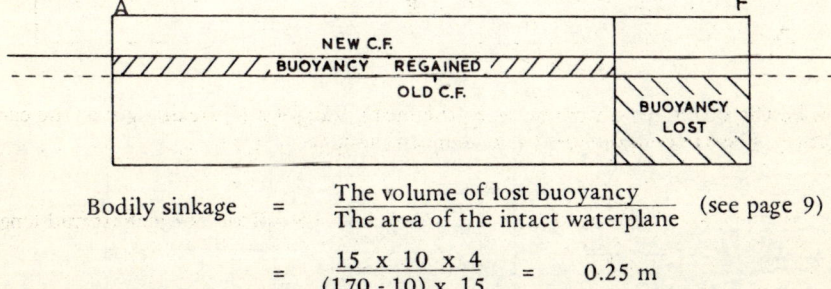

$$\text{Bodily sinkage} \quad = \quad \frac{\text{The volume of lost buoyancy}}{\text{The area of the intact waterplane}} \quad \text{(see page 9)}$$

$$= \quad \frac{15 \times 10 \times 4}{(170 - 10) \times 15} \quad = \quad 0.25 \text{ m}$$

The buoyancy lost at the end is transferred to the intact part of the waterplane. We can for practical purposes treat the buoyancy lost forward as a weight loaded. It should be noted that the position of the tipping centre has changed.

Buoyancy lost	=	$15 \times 10 \times 4 \times 1.025$	=	615 tonnes
The moment caused	=	615×85	=	52275 tonnes-metres
change of trim	=	$\dfrac{\text{Moment caused}}{\text{MCT 1cm}}$	=	$\dfrac{52275}{100}$
			=	522.75 cm by the head
Change of draught for'd =		$\dfrac{522.75 \times 90}{170}$	=	276.75 cm increase
Change of draught aft =		$\dfrac{522.75 \times 80}{170}$	=	246.00 cm decrease

	F	A
Old draught	4.000m	4.000m
Sinkage	0.250m	0.250m
	4.250m	4.250m
Change due to trim	+ 2.768m	- 2.460m
New draughts	7.018m	1.790m

CHANGE OF DRAUGHT WHEN PASSING BETWEEN WATER OF DIFFERENT DENSITIES

When a vessel passes from water of greater density to water of lesser density there will be a bodily sinkage and worked example 2 shows the principles.

In addition to the sinkage there will be a shift in the position of the centre of buoyancy. The centre of buoyancy will move towards the geometrical centre of the extra layer of buoyancy. If the centre of buoyancy is not vertically below the centre of the layer there will be a fore and aft movement of the centre of buoyancy as well as a vertical movement. The centre of flotation can, for practical purposes, be considered as the centre of the layer .

The change in the fore and aft position results in a lever between the forces of gravity and buoyancy which in turn causes a trimming moment, as the vessel is only in longitudinal equilibrium when the centres of gravity and buoyancy are on the same vertical line.

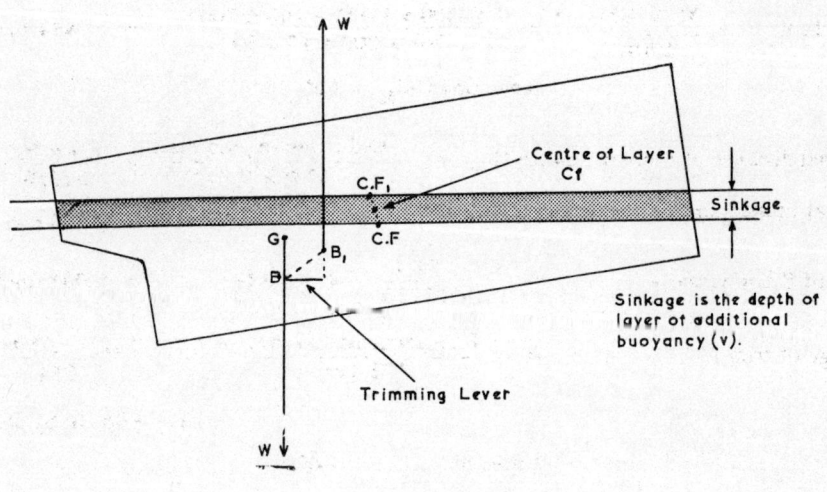

$$BB_1 = \frac{v}{V} \times \text{ distance } BC_f$$

where   v is the volume of layer of additional buoyancy
        V is volume displaced by vessel

The horizontal part of the shift BB_1 is the length of the trimming lever and can be found by multiplying the volume of the layer by the fore and aft distance between the centres of flotation and buoyancy and dividing by the volume of displacement. The trim is always in the opposite direction to the shift of the centre of buoyancy.

Passing from water of less density to that of greater density also affects draught, but in the opposite sense to that described above.

WORKED EXAMPLE 36

A box shaped vessel 200 metres length on the waterline has a breadth of 25 metres and is floating in salt water at draughts of 9.0 metres forward and 11.0 metres aft. Calculate her draughts on passing into fresh water.

Original draught   9.0 m F)
                          11.0 m A)   10.0m mean

Trim   2.0 m by stern   =   200 cm by stern

Volume of displacement in salt water   =   200 x 25 x 10   = $50000 m^3$

Volume of displacement in fresh water   = $50000 \times \dfrac{1.025}{1.000}$ = $51250 m^3$

Volume of layer $1250 m^3$

$$\text{Bodily sinkage} = \frac{\text{Volume of layer}}{\text{Area of layer}} = \frac{1250}{200 \times 25} = 0.25 \text{ m}$$

$$\text{MCT 1 cm} = \frac{W \times GM_L}{100L} = \frac{50000 \times 1.025 \times 200 \times 200}{100 \times 200 \times 12 \times 10} = 854 \text{ t-m}$$

$$\text{(assuming } GM_L = BM_L)$$

Original distance of B abaft midlength   = $\dfrac{\text{Old trimming moment}}{\text{Displacement}}$ = $\dfrac{854 \times 200}{51250}$ m

(C.F. at midlength as waterplane rectangular)

                                           =   3.333 metres

Shift of B horizontally   = $\dfrac{1250}{51250} \times 3.333$ =   0.0813 metres

Change of trim   = $\dfrac{\text{Displacement x Lever}}{\text{MCT 1 cm}}$ = $\dfrac{51250 \times 0.0813}{854}$

                                           =   4.88 cm by stern

	Forward		Aft	
Original draughts	9.000 m		11.000 m	
Bodily sinkage	.250 m		.250 m	
	9.250 m		11.250 m	
Change of draught due to change of trim	.024 m	+	.024 m	½ change of trim as C.F. at midlength in this example.
Draughts in fresh water	9.226 m		11.274 m	

CHAPTER SIX

Drydocking

When a vessel is to drydock it is usual to have her trimmed by the stern. This enables the stern to be set on the blocks, and then used as a pivot to align the keel along the blocks. If the vessel is not trimmed by the stern greater skill will be needed in the manipulation of the mooring tackles forward and aft.

When the vessel first touches the blocks, the whole of the vessel's weight is being supported by the buoyancy of the water. As water is pumped from the dock, part of the buoyancy of the water is transferred to the keel blocks, this is called the UPTHRUST (P). It will be shown that this upthrust causes a loss of GM.

To prevent the loss of GM causing instability:-

     (a)   The vessel should have an adequate GM.

     (b)   Free surface in the tanks should be at a minimum.

     (c)   The vessel should not be trimmed too far by the stern.

The critical time during the drydocking operation is just before the vessel takes the blocks fore and aft. Until she is on the blocks throughout her length, the shores cannot be set up tight, and it should be ensured that she still has positive stability at the time. When the vessel has taken the blocks overall pumping of the dock ceases until the shores have been set up tight.

When placing the shores on the ship's side, it should be seen that the end of the shore is over a frame and, if possible, at the intersection of a frame and a deck stringer, as the greater strength is at this point.

A critical time also occurs when refloating. The distribution of weight should be similar to that when the vessel drydocked. Tank soundings should be taken as soon as the vessel has taken the blocks overall. Similar soundings should be obtained before refloating.

If any tank plugs in the bottom of the vessel have been removed the mate should see that they have been replaced before the dock is flooded.

Whilst in drydock a fire hose from the shore should be connected to the ship's fire main. All discharges overside should be stopped.

TO FIND THE UPTHRUST

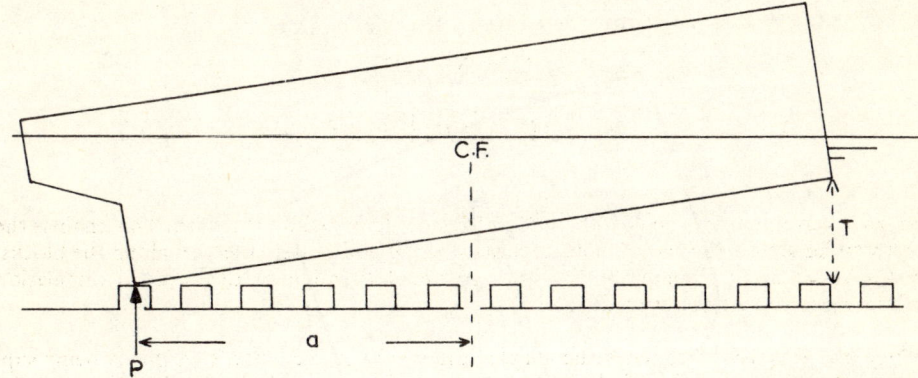

In the diagram above

      P is the upthrust

      a is the distance of the sternpost from the centre of flotation

      T is the trim

In order to have the vessel on the blocks fore and aft, a moment has to be caused to change the trim T centimetres. This moment could be caused by loading a weight forward of the C.F., discharging a weight from abaft the C.F., shifting a weight from aft to forward or pushing up at the after part of the ship.

The last named method is virtually what the upthrust does. The moment it causes is P x a.

Then:	The moment caused	=	The moment to be caused.
i.e.	P x a	=	T x MCT 1cm
so	P	=	$\dfrac{T \times MCT\ 1cm}{a}$

Note: This is the upthrust at the instant the stem takes the blocks.

The upthrust at any time prior to this can be found by substituting the change of trim up to that time for T in the equation above.

When a vessel is on the blocks and on an even keel, the upthrust will increase by an amount equal to the TPC for every centimetre of water that is pumped out of the dock.

      i.e.   P = TPC x the number of centimetres the water has fallen.

TO FIND THE LOSS OF G.M.

Consider the vessel heeled to an angle θ°

θ° can be the smallest angle that there is (e.g. 1 second of arc)

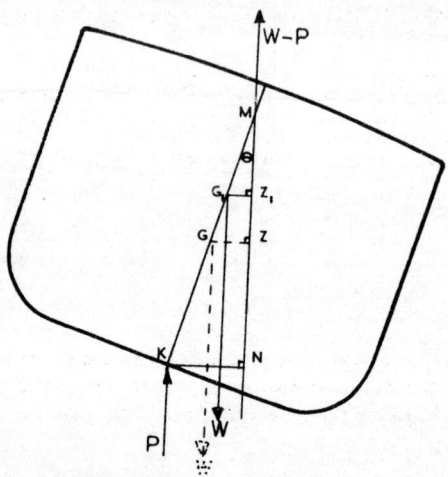

Taking moments about M (considering it to be fixed)

$$W \times GZ \;-\; P \times KN \;=\; W \times G_1 Z_1$$

or $W \times GM \sin \theta - P \times KM \sin \theta \;=\; W \times G_1 M \sin \theta$

then $W (GM - G_1 M) \;=\; P \times KM$

i.e. $GM - G_1 M \;=\; \dfrac{P \times KM}{W}$

(or the loss of GM)

Alternatively if P is considered as a weight discharged from the keel, the shift of G or loss of GM can be found by taking moments about G.

Then   The loss of GM $=\; \dfrac{P \times KG}{W - P}$

Either of the above approximate formulae may be used in working out problems.

Whilst there is a difference in the effective GM and therefore the GZ there will be practically no difference in the Righting Moment which is the important quantity in ship stability. The reason that the righting moments will be the same is because the different GZs will be multiplied by different displacements - using the first formula the displacement will be W, whereas it will be W - P when using the second formula.

WORKED EXAMPLE 37

A vessel of 3000 tonnes displacement, KM (considered fixed) 4.5 metres MCT 1cm 80 tonnes-metres is trimmed 50 cm by the stern. The sternpost is 40 metres abaft the centre of flotation. Calculate the loss of GM at the instant the stem takes the blocks.

$$P = \frac{C \text{ of } T \times MCT \text{ 1cm}}{a} = \frac{50 \times 80}{40} = 100 \text{ tonnes}$$

$$\text{Loss of GM} = \frac{P \times KM}{W} = \frac{100 \times 4.5}{3000} = 0.15 \text{ metres}$$

WORKED EXAMPLE 38

A vessel of 4000 tonnes displacement TPC 12, KM (considered fixed) 4.2m, KG 3.2m is on an even keel. She enters drydock and is set down on to the blocks. What is her effective GM when a further 0.45 metres of water is pumped from the dock?

P = TPC x cm of water pumped out

  = 12 x 45

  = 540 tonnes

$$\text{Loss of GM} = \frac{P \times KM}{W} = \frac{540 \times 4.2}{4000} = 0.567 \text{ m}$$

$$\text{Old GM} = 1.000 \text{ m}$$

$$\text{Effective GM} = \overline{0.433 \text{ m}}$$

Alternatively:-

$$\text{Loss of GM} = \frac{P \times KG}{W - P} = \frac{540 \times 3.2}{3460} = 0.499 \text{ m}$$

$$\text{Old GM} = 1.000 \text{ m}$$

$$\text{Effective GM} = \overline{0.501 \text{ m}}$$

CHAPTER SEVEN

Water Pressure

PRESSURE is force per unit area, and in this section the force is due to a head of liquid.

Consider an area of one square metre 1 metre under the surface of fresh water. The volume of water over the area is $1m^3$. From the previous work in chapter one it is known that this weighs 1 tonne or 1000 kgf and therefore the pressure is $1000 \text{ kgf}/m^2$. If the depth of fresh water over the same area is increased to 2 metres the volume of water will be increased to $2m^3$ which weighs 2 tonnes or 2000 kgf so the pressure now is $2000 \text{ kgf}/m^2$. If the depth of water is further increased the pressure will also increase, therefore pressure can be said to vary directly with depth. The depth in the case of horizontal areas is also the pressure head, further mention of pressure head is made on the next page.

If the water had been other than fresh its weight per cubic metre would have been greater than 1 tonne and if a liquid with a density less than that of fresh water had been used its weight per cubic metre would have been less than 1 tonne. The pressure would also have been different from that for fresh water so pressure varies directly with the density, or in practical terms the relative density.

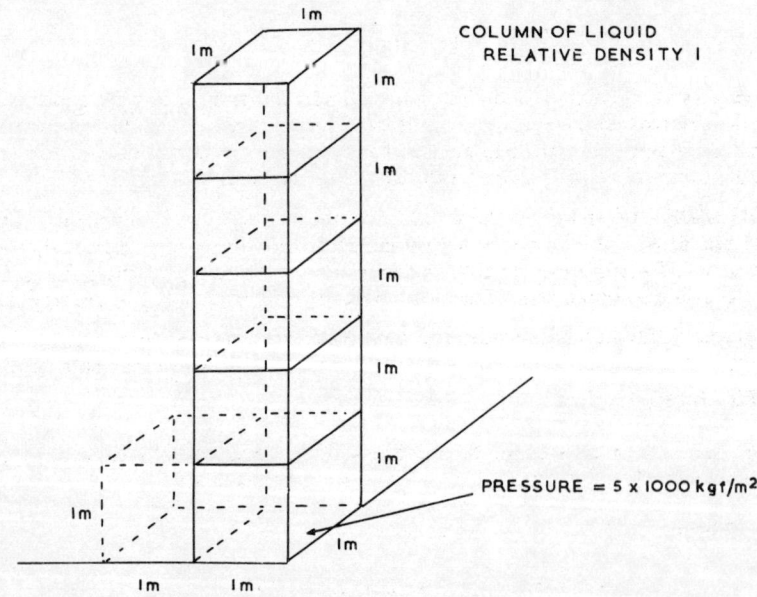

COLUMN OF LIQUID
RELATIVE DENSITY 1

PRESSURE = 5 x 1000 kgf/m²

Increasing the area under water will increase the volume of water over the area. Suppose the depth of water remains constant at 1 metre whilst the area under the water is increased to 5 metres. The weight of water over the area is 5 tonnes or 5000 kgf, but the weight per unit area is only $\frac{5000}{5}$ kgf/m^2 or 1000 kgf/m^2. So the pressure is quite independent of the area under pressure, but the weight over the whole area depends on the area under pressure. The total weight of liquid over an area is called the THRUST.

To summarise.

The thrust on an area   =   A x h x δ tonnes

Where   A is the area under pressure in square metres
          h is the pressure head in metres
          δ is the density of the liquid in tonnes per cubic metre

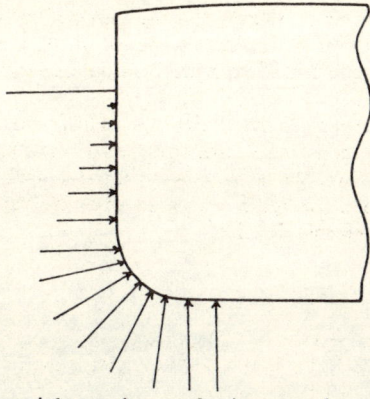

The thrust always acts at right angles to the immersed surface and for any set depth the thrust upwards, downwards, sideways and any other direction will be exactly the same. It can be shown that the pressure head to be used for obtaining the thrust on any area is the depth of the geometrical centre of the area below the surface of the liquid.

CENTRE OF PRESSURE of an area is the point on the area where the total thrust could be considered to act. It will not be necessary to calculate this point. However, it should be borne in mind that if a bulkhead requires shoring due to flooding on the other side, the most effective point to place the shore is at the centre of pressure. For rectangular areas vertically placed (ordinary bulkheads) the centre of pressure is $\frac{2}{3}$ depth below the surface. For triangular areas (collision bulkheads) the centre of pressure is at half depth.

WORKED EXAMPLE 39

A double bottom tank 20 metres long, 15 metres wide is being tested with a head of 2.5 metres of salt water. Calculate the thrust on the tanktop plating.

Thrust   =   A x h x δ

            =   20 x 15 x 2.5 x 1.025

            =   768.75 tonnes

WORKED EXAMPLE 40

A rectangular lock gate 20 metres wide, 15 metres deep, has 6 metres of water R.D. 1.025 on one side, whilst on the other side there is 10 metres of water R.D. 1.012. Calculate the thrust on each side.

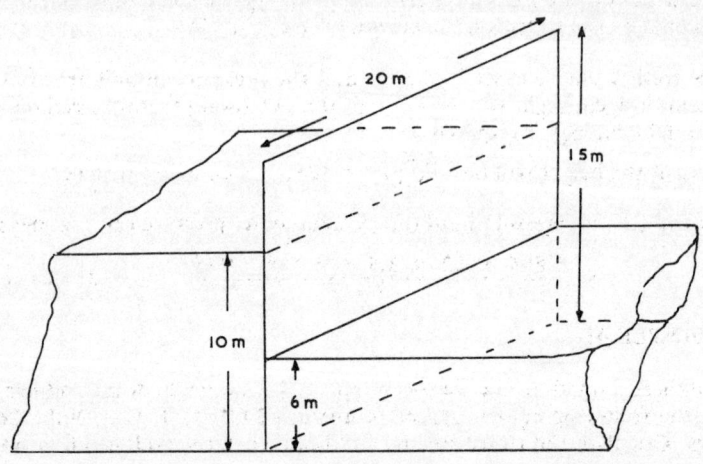

Salt water side

$$\begin{aligned}
\text{Thrust} &= A \times h \times \delta \\
&= 20 \times 6 \times 3 \times 1.025 \\
&= 369 \text{ tonnes}
\end{aligned}$$

Other side

$$\begin{aligned}
\text{Thrust} &= A \times h \times \delta \\
&= 20 \times 10 \times 5 \times 1.012 \\
&= \underline{1012 \text{ tonnes}}
\end{aligned}$$

WORKED EXAMPLE 41

Calculate the upthrust on the bottom plating of a box shaped vessel 75 metres long, 10 metres wide, 7 metres deep, when floating at a draught of 5 metres in fresh water.

$$\begin{aligned}
\text{Thrust} &= A \times h \times \delta \\
&= 75 \times 10 \times 5 \times 1.000 \\
&= \underline{3750 \text{ tonnes}}
\end{aligned}$$

It will be noted that this thrust on the bottom is the same as the vessel's displacement. This is as one would expect, as the principle of flotation is that the upthrust due to buoyancy is equal to the vessel's displacement.

WORKED EXAMPLE 42

A cylindrical pressure vessel for the carriage of compressed gases has a length of 12 metres and a diameter of 7 metres and is fitted vertically in a ship. The maximum pressure to which the top is to be subject is 0.6 kgf/cm^2. If the top of the cylinder is to be water tested with salt water to this pressure how far up the stand pipe would the water be, and what would be the thrust on the cylinder top at this time?

If the water is fresh 1 cm^3 weighs 1 gramme and the pressure on unit area is 1 gf/cm^2 when the column is 1 cm high. If a pressure of 0.6 kgf (600 gf) is required on unit area (cm^2) a column 600 cm high is required.

As the water is salt the height will be $\dfrac{600}{1.025}$ cm = 585.4 cm or 5.854 metres

thrust on tank top (t) = pressure head (m) x area under pressure (m^2) x density

$$= \frac{5.854 \times 22 \times 3.5 \times 3.5 \times 1.025}{7} = 231.01 \text{ tonnes}$$

WORKED EXAMPLE 43

A collision bulkhead bounding the forepeak tank is 24 metres in depth and has, starting from the top, the following equally spaced ordinates:- 34.0, 33.3, 32.5, 30.8, 26.5, 17.3 and 6.2 metres. Calculate the thrust on the bulkhead when the tank is full of water R.D. 1.016.

No. of ordinate	Ordinate	x S.M.	= Product for Area	x Lever	= Product for moment
1	34.0	1	34.0	0	0
2	33.3	4	133.2	1	133.2
3	32.5	2	65.0	2	130.0
4	30.8	4	123.2	3	369.6
5	26.5	2	53.0	4	212.0
6	17.3	4	69.2	5	346.0
7	6.2	1	6.2	6	37.2
		Sum of the Products	483.8		Sum 1228.0

$$\frac{4}{3}$$

Bulkhead area   645.07m^2

Geometrical centre of the area below the surface $= \dfrac{1228 \times 4}{483.8} = 10.153$ metres

Thrust = Area x Pressure

= 645.07 x 10.153 x 1.016

= 6654.3 tonnes

CHAPTER EIGHT

Free Surface Effects

Whenever there is a surface of liquid which is free to move, there is a loss of effective GM. This loss takes place irrespective of the position of the free surface in the ship.

As can be seen from the diagram below, the movement of liquid in the tank caused a shift, to the low side, of the ship's centre of gravity. The tank is shown to be half full of water and for the angle of heel illustrated, its centre of gravity will shift from g to g_1.

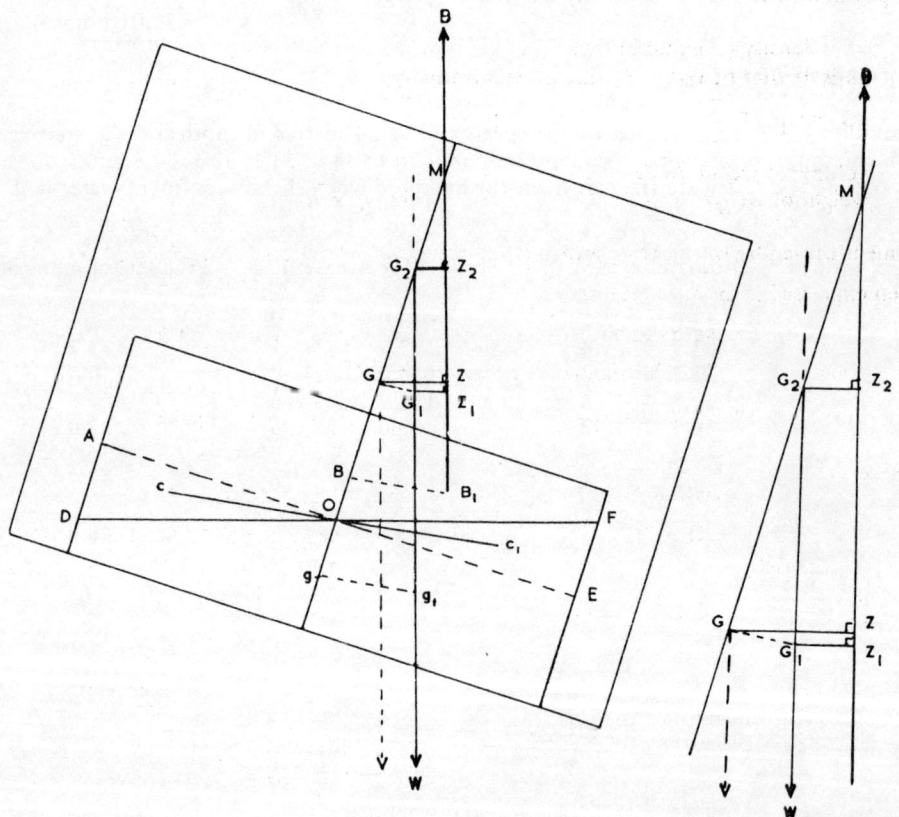

If the tank is more than half full, then for the same angle of heel, the movement of its centre of gravity will be less. Conversely if the tank is less than half full there will be a greater movement of its centre of gravity.

When G shifts to G_1 there is a reduction in the righting lever from that which there would be if there were no free surface (B_1 remaining fixed as the angle of heel and displacement do not change). The effective righting lever now is G_1Z_1. The righting lever is the perpendicular distance between the forces of gravity and buoyancy and can be drawn at any convenient point. When considering free surface effect it is convenient to draw the righting lever from the point where the line of action of gravity cuts the centre line of the vessel; this point is G_2. G_2Z_2 is the equal to G_1Z_1 so G_2M is the effective GM. G_2 is the virtual position of the ship's centre of gravity (note the actual position is at G_1) and GG_2 is the virtual loss of GM due to the free surface effect.

Let l be the length of the free surface
and b be the breadth of the free surface then $\dfrac{b}{2}$ = ½ breadth = AO = OE = y

c and c_1 are centres of gravity of wedges of liquid in original position (AOD) and transferred position (EOF) when the vessel is heeled $\theta°$ (a small angle).

δt is density of liquid in tank
δs is density of water in which vessel is floating

$$cO = C_1 0 \simeq \frac{2}{3}y \qquad\qquad \text{so } cc_1 \simeq \frac{4}{3}y$$

volume of wedge AOD $\qquad = \quad y\tan\theta° \times \dfrac{y}{2} \times l$
weight of wedge $\qquad\qquad = \quad$ volume x δt

moment caused by transferring wedge from c to c_1 = ½$y^2\tan\theta° \times l \times \delta t \times \dfrac{4}{3}y$

when expressed in circular measure $\tan\theta°$ $\qquad = \qquad \theta_R$

so moment $\qquad\qquad\qquad\qquad = \quad \dfrac{2}{3}y^3 \times l \times \theta_R \times \delta t$

but this moment causes a shift of G to G_1

such that GG_1 $\qquad\qquad\qquad = \quad \dfrac{\frac{2}{3}y^3 \times l \times \theta_R \times \delta t}{V \times \delta s}$

Where $V \times \delta s$ $\qquad\qquad = \quad$ Vessel's displacement

Also GG_1 $\qquad\qquad\qquad = \quad GG_2 \times \theta_R$

$\therefore \quad GG_2 \times \theta_R$ $\qquad\qquad = \quad \dfrac{\frac{2}{3}y^3 \times l \times \theta_R \times \delta t}{V \times \delta s}$

as $\dfrac{2}{3}y^3 \times l$ $\qquad\qquad = \quad$ moment of inertia free of surface (i)

GG_2 $\qquad\qquad\qquad\qquad = \quad \dfrac{i}{V} \times \dfrac{\delta t}{\delta s}$ $\quad$ or $\dfrac{i}{W} \times \delta t$

where y = ½ breadth of rectangular free surface $\qquad i = \dfrac{2}{3} \times (\dfrac{b}{2})^3 \times l = \dfrac{lb^3}{12}$

if the free surface is divided longitudinally it can be shown that the virtual loss of GM (GG_2) varies inversely as the square of the number (n) of compartment.

so that $\qquad GG_2$ $\qquad\qquad\qquad = \quad \dfrac{i}{V} \times \dfrac{\delta t}{\delta s} \times \dfrac{1}{n^2}$ $\quad$ or $\dfrac{i}{W} \times \dfrac{\delta t}{n^2}$

WORKED EXAMPLE 44

A vessel displacing 8000 tonnes in salt water has a double bottom tank 20 metres long and 16 metres wide, partly full of sea water. If the ship's KM is 7 metres and the KG is 6 metres, calculate the effective GM if (a) the D.B. is undivided, (b) there is a centre line division, (c) there is a centre line division and two watertight side girders.

(a)

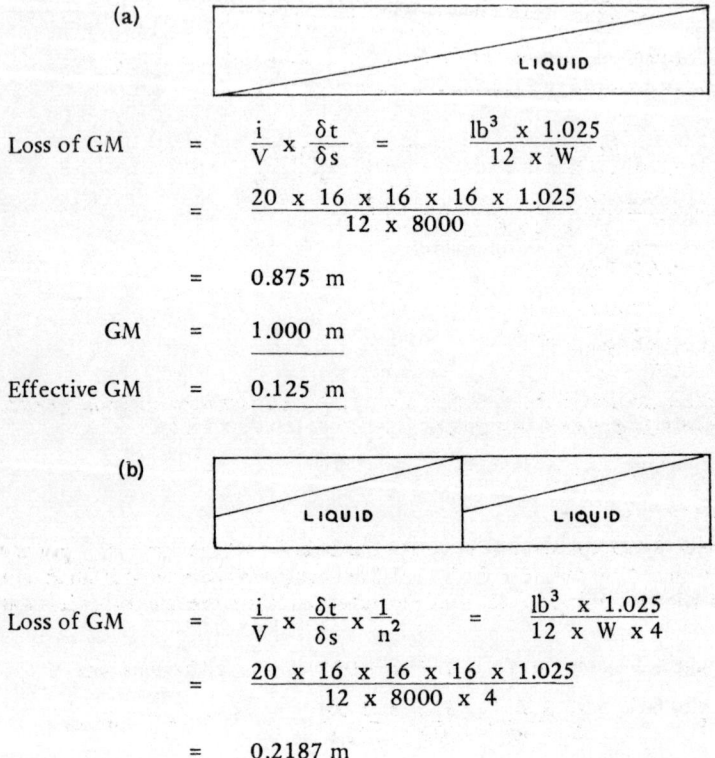

$$\text{Loss of GM} = \frac{i}{V} \times \frac{\delta t}{\delta s} = \frac{lb^3 \times 1.025}{12 \times W}$$

$$= \frac{20 \times 16 \times 16 \times 16 \times 1.025}{12 \times 8000}$$

$$= 0.875 \text{ m}$$

$$\text{GM} = \underline{1.000 \text{ m}}$$

$$\text{Effective GM} = \underline{0.125 \text{ m}}$$

(b)

$$\text{Loss of GM} = \frac{i}{V} \times \frac{\delta t}{\delta s} \times \frac{1}{n^2} = \frac{lb^3 \times 1.025}{12 \times W \times 4}$$

$$= \frac{20 \times 16 \times 16 \times 16 \times 1.025}{12 \times 8000 \times 4}$$

$$= 0.2187 \text{ m}$$

$$\text{GM} = \underline{1.0000 \text{ m}}$$

$$\text{Effective GM} = \underline{0.7813 \text{ m}}$$

OR each tank could be taken separately.

$$\text{Then loss of GM for each tank} = \frac{20 \times 8 \times 8 \times 8 \times 1.025}{12 \times 8000}$$

$$= 0.1093 \text{ m}$$

$$\text{For both tanks} = 0.2187 \text{ m}$$

(c)

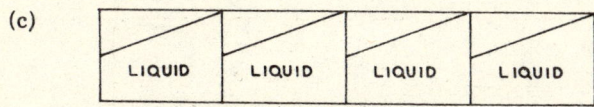

$$\text{Loss of GM} = \frac{i}{V} \times \frac{\delta t}{\delta s} \times \frac{1}{n^2} = \frac{lb^3 \times 1.025}{12 \times W \times 16}$$

$$= \frac{20 \times 16 \times 16 \times 16 \times 1.025}{12 \times 8000 \times 16}$$

$$= 0.0547 \text{ m}$$

$$\text{GM} = \underline{1.0000 \text{ m}}$$

$$\text{Effective GM} = \underline{0.9453 \text{ m}}$$

The foregoing example emphasises the fact that the greater the number of subdivisions, the smaller is the loss of GM due to free surface.

WORKED EXAMPLE 45

A ship of displacement 1400 tonnes has 2 metres freeboard with her centre of gravity 0.2m above the waterline. A rectangular deck area 20m long and 10m wide is filled to a depth of 0.5m when the vessel ships a sea. Find the effect on the vessel's righting lever at $5°$ heel.

$$\text{weight of water shipped} = 20 \times 10 \times 0.5 \times 1.025 = 102.5 \text{ tonnes}$$

$$\text{rise of G due to above} = \frac{w \times d}{W + w} = \frac{102.5 \times 2.05}{1400 + 102.5} = 0.1397 \text{ metres}$$

$$\text{loss of GM due to free surface} = \frac{i}{V} \times \frac{\delta t}{\delta s} \times \frac{1}{n^2} = \frac{20 \times 10 \times 10 \times 10 \times 1.025}{12 \times \dfrac{1502.5}{1.025} \times 1.025}$$

$$= 1.1369 \text{ m}$$

The total effect on the GM is an effective loss of 0.1397 + 1.1369 metres i.e. 1.2766m ∴ the effect is to decrease the GZ at $5°$ by 1.2766 x sin $5°$ i.e. 0.11127 metres.

As can be seen this is a significant reduction in initial stability and with such possible reductions in mind the 1968 Load Line Rules require that vessels shall have a certain minimum stability and these requirements are given on page 97.

WORKED EXAMPLE 46

A vessel KM 8.0m, KG 7.0m, displacing 9171 tonnes in water relative density 1.019 has a double bottom tank, longitudinally divided, 20m long, 15m wide and 1.2m deep, filled with oil relative density 0.95. Calculate the effective GM if half the oil is used.

$$\text{Weight discharged} = 20 \times 15 \times 0.6 \times 0.95$$

$$= 171.0 \text{ tonnes}$$

$$\text{KG ship} = 7.00 \text{ m}$$

$$\text{KG oil} = 0.90 \text{ m}$$

$$d = 6.10 \text{ m}$$

$$GG_1 = \frac{w \times d}{W - w} = \frac{171.0 \times 6.1}{9171 - 171} = \frac{1043.1}{9000} = 0.116 \text{ metres}$$

$$\text{Loss due to free surface} = \frac{i}{V} \times \frac{\delta t}{\delta s} \times \frac{1}{n^2}$$

$$= \frac{\frac{1b^3}{12 \times W}}{\delta s} \times \frac{\delta t}{\delta s} \times \frac{1}{n^2}$$

$$= \frac{20 \times 15 \times 15 \times 15 \times 0.95}{12 \times 9000 \times 4}$$

$$= \underline{0.148 \text{ metres}}$$

$$\begin{aligned}
\text{KM} &= 8.000 \text{ metres} \\
\text{KG} &= 7.000 \text{ metres} \\
\text{Original GM} &= 1.000 \text{ metres} \\
GG_1 &= \underline{0.116 \text{ metres}} \\
& 0.884 \text{ metres} \\
\text{Free surface loss} &= \underline{0.148 \text{ metres}} \\
\text{Effective GM} &= \underline{0.736 \text{ metres}}
\end{aligned}$$

It must be emphasised that free surfaces of liquid can be dangerous and they should be kept at a minimum at all times.

If there is any doubt about a vessel's stability, do not try to rectify a tendency to instability by haphazardly filling double bottom tanks. It must be remembered that before G is brought down due to increased weight in the bottom there will be a virtual rise due to the effect of free surface.

Information about the loss of GM due to free surface must be provided on all vessels whose keels are laid after the 19th November, 1952. This is usually given as a free surface moment, which has to be divided by the displacement of the vessel in order to get the loss of GM.

CHAPTER NINE
Stability Data

The Load Line Rules require minimum stability conditions as follows:-

(a)   The area under the curve of Righting Levers (GZ curve) shall not be less than -

    (i)   0.055 metre-radians up to an angle of 30 degrees.

    (ii)   0.09 metre-radians up to an angle of either 40 degrees or the angle at which the lower edges of any openings in the hull, superstructures or deckhouses, being openings which cannot be closed weathertight, are immersed if that angle be less.

    (iii)   0.03 metre-radians between the angles of heel of 30 degrees and 40 degrees or such lesser angle as is referred to in (ii).

(b)   The Righting Lever (GZ) shall be at least 0.20 metres at an angle of heel equal to or greater than 30 degrees.

(c)   The maximum Righting Lever (GZ) shall occur at an angle of heel not less than 30 degrees.

(d)   The initial transverse metacentric height shall not be less than 0.15 metres. In the case of a ship carrying a timber deck cargo which complies with subparagraph (a) by taking into account the volume of timber deck cargo the initial transverse metacentric height shall not be less than 0.05 metres.

The GZ curve referred to above is also known as a curve of statical stability and is described below.

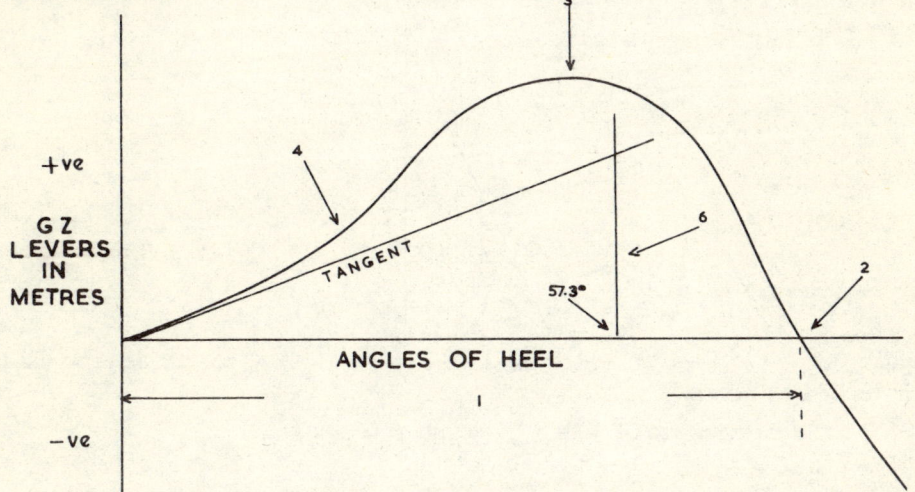

When GZ levers are plotted against angles of heel a curve of statical stability is formed. This is illustrated on the previous page. The information which can be obtained from the curve is detailed below.

1.   The range of stability.

2.   The angle of vanishing stability.

3.   The maximum GZ lever and the angle at which it occurs.

4.   The point at which the deck edge immerses (this is known as the point of contraflexure, i.e. where the shape of the curve changes from concave to convex, when viewed from above).

5.   The dynamical stability, this is found by multiplying the area under the curve by the vessel's displacement (see worked example 47).

6.   The approximate GM. A tangent is drawn to the curve at its origin, and a vertical line is drawn from the base line at $57.3°$. The distance above the base line of the point where the vertical line and the tangent intersect is the GM. (This is measured on the GZ scale.)

$$\left(GM = \frac{GZ}{\sin \theta°} \quad \text{or} \quad \frac{GZ}{\theta \text{ Radians}} \right)$$

$$1 \text{ Radian} = 57.3°$$

Strictly speaking we should be given the GM so as to get the direction of the curve at its origin, but questions may be asked involving the finding of it.

It will be seen that GZ levers are plotted against angles of heel, and it should be understood that when a curve of statical stability is drawn, it only applies to the vessel for the one condition of loading at which it is drawn.

EFFECT OF POSITION OF G on a curve of statical stability.

It can be seen from the figure below that when G is raised to G_1 the GZ lever is reduced by y metres. Also it can be seen that $y = GG_1 \sin \theta°$

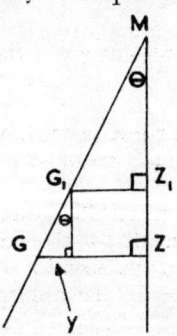

Similarly if the centre of gravity was lowered from G_1 to G the GZ lever would be increased by y metres.

So the change in GZ   =   The shift of G x $\sin \theta°$.

EFFECT OF FREEBOARD on a curve of statical stability.

The more freeboard that a vessel has, then the greater the angle to which she can be inclined without immersing the deck edge. This is shown below.

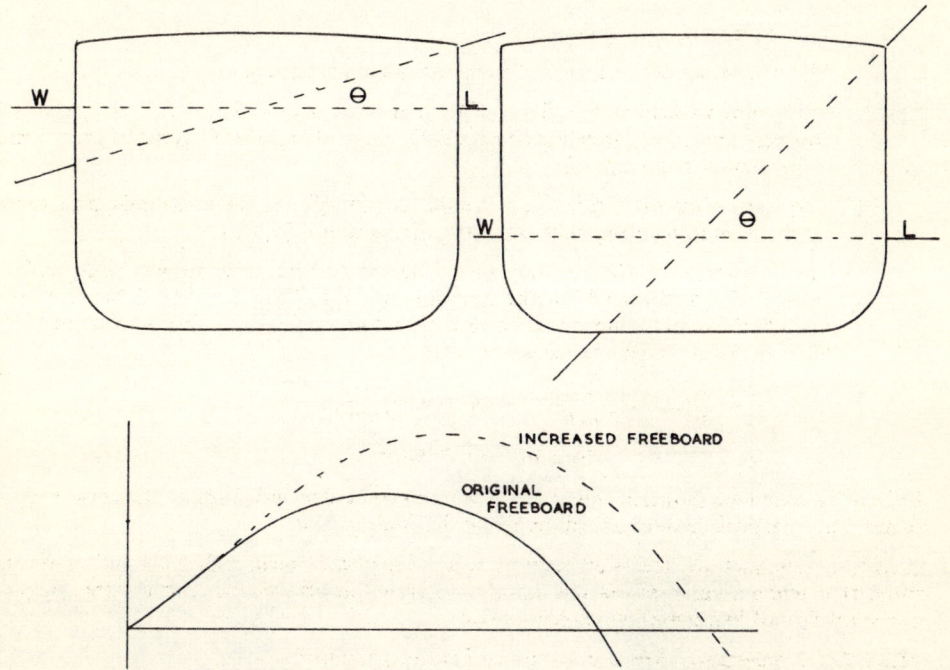

When the freeboard is increased the range of stability is also increased. This gives greater dynamical stability.

It should also be noted that V is smaller when the freeboard is larger and so BM is greater (assuming I to be constant).

To avoid the necessity of carrying a curve for each of the vessel's possible displacements, a set of cross curves is drawn. A specimen set of them is illustrated on page 101).

In order to produce a curve of statical stability from the cross curves, the GZ levers for the various angles of heel are taken off for the required displacement. These are then corrected for any difference between the position of the ship's centre of gravity and the centre of gravity for which the curves are drawn. Finally the GZ levers are plotted against the angle of heel. The worked example on page 102 should make this clear

Sometimes the curve of statical stability is drawn with righting moments instead of GZ levers on the ordinate. The curve can be useful in this form as one can see at a glance how much the vessel will heel when an upsetting moment is applied. The upsetting moment may be caused by transverse movement of weight or, particularly with passenger ships, the effect of a strong wind blowing on the ship's side.

EFFECT OF BEAM on a curve of statical stability

This must be considered in the design stage.

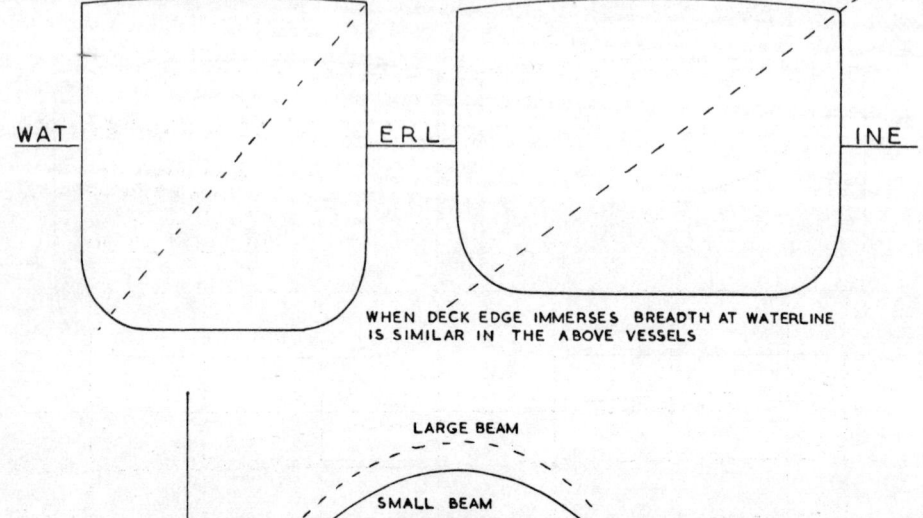

WHEN DECK EDGE IMMERSES BREADTH AT WATERLINE
IS SIMILAR IN THE ABOVE VESSELS

It has already been stated that BM $= \dfrac{I}{V}$ and provided that V remains constant BM varies with I. I is largely dependent on the breadth of the waterplane, so an increase in beam will increase BM. This in turn increases GZ. The effect is most noticeable at the smaller angles of inclination.

The case of a vessel having a negative GM in the upright position was discussed on page 52. The first part of her statical stability curve would appear as under.

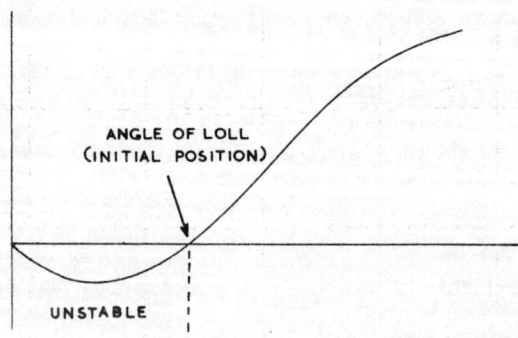

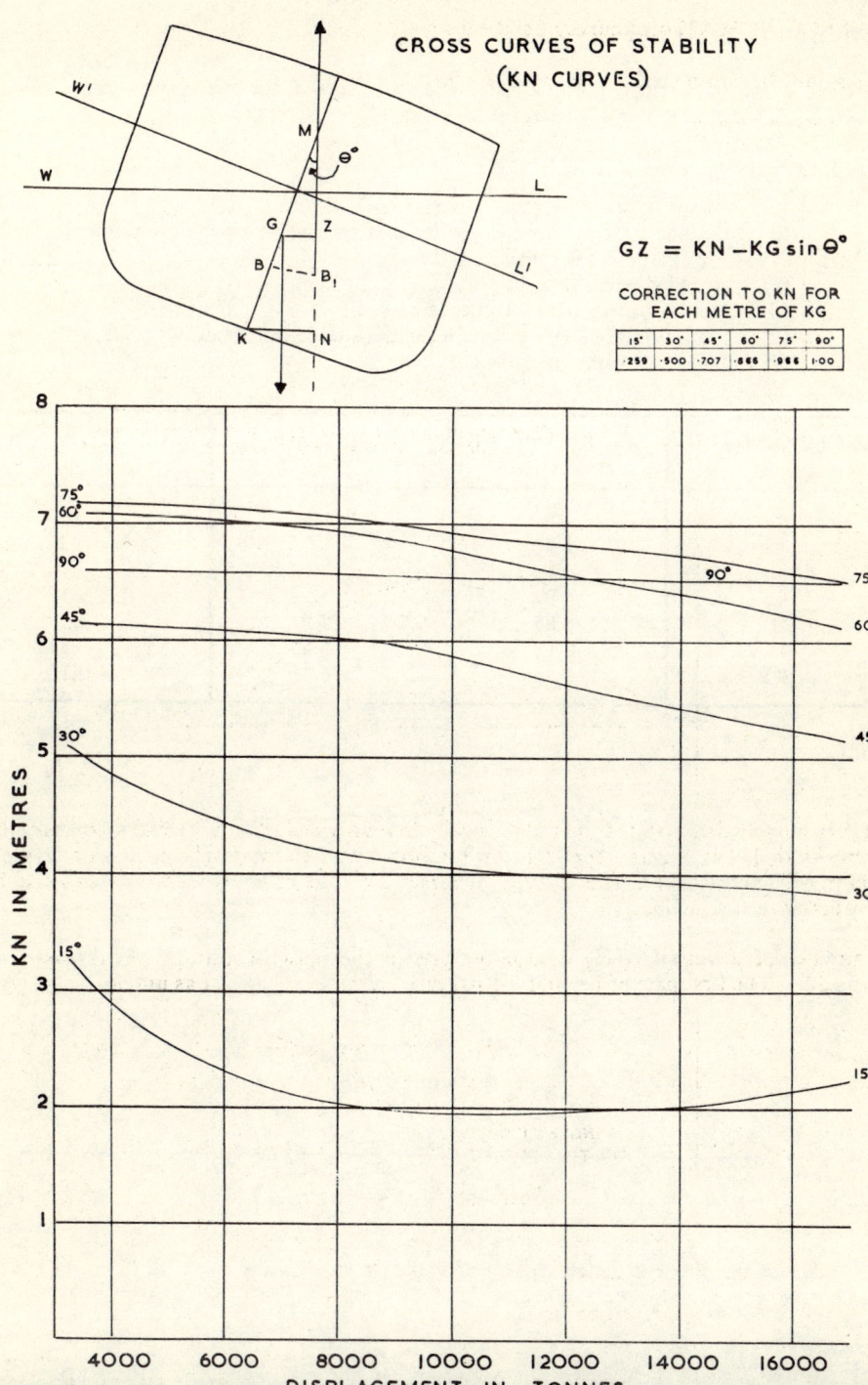

CROSS CURVES OF STABILITY
(KN CURVES)

$$GZ = KN - KG \sin \Theta°$$

CORRECTION TO KN FOR
EACH METRE OF KG

15°	30°	45°	60°	75°	90°
·259	·500	·707	·866	·966	1·00

KN IN METRES

DISPLACEMENT IN TONNES

WORKED EXAMPLE 47

Draw a curve of statical stability, using the cross curves, for the vessel when displacing 9000 tonnes with a KG of 6.7 metres.

From the curve give the following.

- (a)   Range of stability.
- (b)   Change of the above range when a transverse upsetting moment of 2250 tonnes-metres is caused.
- (c)   Approximate GM.
- (d)   Moment of statical stability if heeled $5°$.
- (e)   Approximate angle at which the deck edge immerses.
- (f)   Dynamical stability at $48°$.

ANGLE OF HEEL	KN from cross curves	KG sin $\theta°$	GZ in metres
$0°$	0	0	0
$15°$	1.98	1.73	0.25
$30°$	4.1	3.35	0.75
$45°$	5.92	4.74	1.18
$60°$	6.82	5.8	1.02
$75°$	6.98	6.47	0.51
$90°$	6.58	6.7	- 0.12

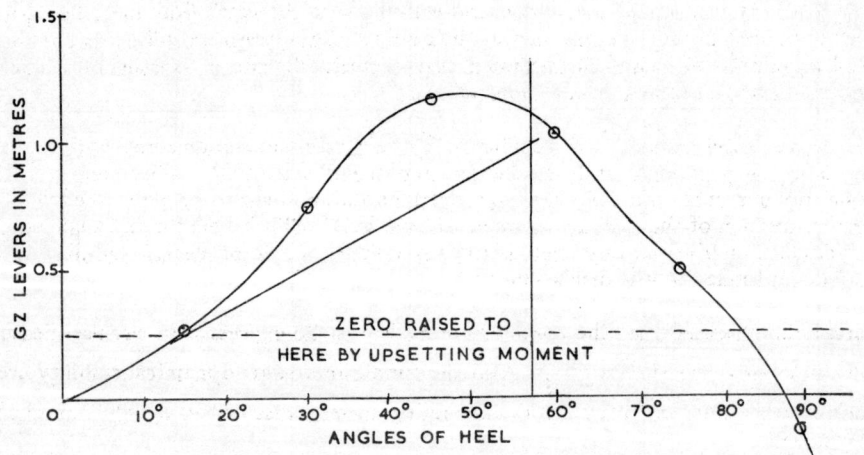

In order to get a curve which will be of value, it is advisable to make 0.5m on the GZ scale equal to about $15°$ on the heel scale.

ANSWERS

(a) $0° - 87°$

(b)   Reduced to $14½° - 81½°$ (divide moment caused by the displacement to obtain reduction in GZ).

(c)   1.00 metres

(d)   675 tonnes-metres (i.e. W x GZ at $5°$).

(e) $26°$

(f)

Heel	GZ in metres	SM	Product for Area
$0°$	0	1	0
$8°$	0.12	4	0.48
$16°$	0.30	2	0.60
$24°$	0.54	4	2.16
$32°$	0.82	2	1.64
$40°$	1.11	4	4.44
$48°$	1.20	1	1.20

$$10.52$$

$$\frac{1}{3}h \text{ in radians} = \frac{8°}{3 \text{ x } 57.3°} = 0.04654 \quad \begin{array}{c} \text{x } 0.04654 \\ \hline \text{Area} = 0.4896 \text{ metre radians} \end{array}$$

$$\text{Dynamical stability} = 0.4896 \text{ x } 9000$$

$$= \underline{4406.4 \text{ tonnes-metres}}$$

(Note: $48°$ can be divided into any convenient number of intervals, 6 or 8 making the calculation simple).

On page 47 it was stated that dynamical stability was the work done in inclining the vessel by external forces and that it was the product of the vessel's displacement and the vertical separation of B and G. Although this is perfectly true it is easier to calculate dynamical stability by the method shown above.

Think of the vessel heeled $1°$, to heel her to $2°$ one would have to do some work to overcome the righting moment at $1°$. If she has now been heeled to $2°$, to heel her to $3°$ the righting moment at $2°$ must be overcome and the total moment to be overcome from the upright is the sum of the righting moments from 0 to $3°$. This is true for any angle and so the dynamical stability at any angle is the area under a curve of statical stability up to that angle multiplied by the displacement.

It must be emphasised that the common interval must be expressed in circular measure and $\theta°$ in circular measure is $\frac{\theta°}{57.3°}$. Also the tonnes-metres of dynamical stability are a measure of work done and are not the same units as the tonnes-metres by which moments are expressed.

Readers must be very careful when using cross curves of stability to note as to whether they are KN curves as shown on page 101 or GZ curves - the older method of presentation.

CARRIAGE OF STABILITY INFORMATION

The provision of stability information for the use of ship's personnel has been required for some years and the minimum requirements were formerly stated in notice M.375. These requirements, with some additions, have now been incorporated in the 1968 Load Line Rules and/are reproduced below.

1.   The ship's name, official number, port of registry, gross and register tonnages, principal dimensions, displacement, deadweight and draught to the Summer load line.

2.   A profile view and, if the Board so require in a particular case, plan views of the ship drawn to scale showing with their names all compartments, tanks, storerooms and crew and passenger accommodation spaces, and also showing the midlength position.

3.   The capacity and the centre of gravity (longitudinally and vertically) of every compartment available for the carriage of cargo, fuel, stores, feed water, domestic water or water ballast.

In the case of a vehicle ferry, the vertical centre of gravity of compartments for the carriage of vehicles shall be based on the estimated centre of gravity of the vehicles and not on the volumetric centres of the compartments.

4.   The estimated total weight of (a) passengers and their effects and (b) crew and their effects, and the centre of gravity (longitudinally and vertically) of each such total weight. In assessing such centres of gravity passengers and crew shall be assumed to be distributed about the ship in the spaces they will normally occupy, including the highest decks to which either or both have access.

5.   The estimated weight and the disposition and centre of gravity of the maximum amount of deck cargo which the ship may reasonably be expected to carry on an exposed deck. The estimated weight shall include in the case of deck cargo likely to absorb water the estimated weight of water likely to be so absorbed and allowed for in arrival conditions, such weight in the case of timber deck cargo being taken to be 15 per cent by weight.

6.   A diagram or scale showing the load line mark and load lines with particulars of the corresponding freeboards, and also showing the displacement, metric tons per centimetre immersion, and deadweight corresponding in each case to a range of mean draughts extending between the waterline representing the deepest load line and the waterline of the ship in light condition.

7.   A diagram or tabular statement showing the hydrostatic particulars of the ship, including:-
     (1)   the heights of the transverse metacentre and
     (2)   the values of the moment to change trim one centimetre,
for a range of mean draughts extending at least between the waterline representing the deepest load line and the waterline of the ship in light condition. Where a tabular statement is used, the intervals between such draughts shall be sufficiently close to permit accurate interpolation. In the case of ships having raked keels, the same datum for the heights of centres of buoyancy and metacentres shall be used as for the centres of gravity referred to in paragraphs 3, 4 and 5.

8.   The effect on stability of free surface in each tank in the ship in which liquids may be carried, including an example to show how the metacentric height is to be corrected.

9.   (1)   A diagram showing cross curves of stability indicating the height of the assumed axis from which the Righting Levers are measured and the trim which has been assumed. In the case of ships having raked keels, where a datum other than the top of keel has been used the position of the assumed axis shall be clearly defined.

(2)   Subject to the following sub-paragraph, only (a) enclosed superstructures and (b) efficient trunks as defined in paragraph 10 of Schedule 5 shall be taken into account in deriving such curves.

(3)   The following structures may be taken into account in deriving such curves if the Board are satisfied that their location, integrity and means of closure will contribute to the ship's stability:-

(a)   superstructures located above the superstructure deck;
(b)   deckhouses on or above the freeboard deck, whether wholly or in part only;
(c)   hatchway structures on or above the freeboard deck.

Additionally, in the case of a ship carrying timber deck cargo, the volume of the timber deck cargo, or a part thereof, may with the Board's approval be taken into account in deriving a supplementary curve of stability appropriate to the ship when carrying such cargo.

(4)   An example shall be given showing how to obtain a curve of Righting Levers (GZ) from the cross curves of stability.

(5)   Where the buoyancy of a superstructure is to be taken into account in the calculation of stability information to be supplied in the case of a vehicle ferry or similar ship having bow doors, ship's side doors or stern doors, there shall be included in the stability information a specific statement that such doors must be secured weathertight before the ship proceeds to sea and that the cross curves of stability are based upon the assumption that such doors have been so secured.

10.   (1)   The diagram and statements referred to in sub-paragraph (2) of this paragraph shall be provided separately for each of the following conditions of the ship:-

(a)   Light condition. If the ship has permanent ballast, such diagram and statements shall be provided for the ship in light condition both (i) with such ballast, and (ii) without such ballast.
(b)   Ballast condition, both (i) on departure, and (ii) on arrival, it being assumed for the purpose of the latter in this and the following sub-paragraphs that oil fuel, fresh water, consumable stores and the like are reduced to 10 per cent of their capacity.
(c)   Condition both (i) on departure, and (ii) on arrival, when loaded to the Summer loadline with cargo filling all spaces available for cargo, cargo for this purpose being taken to be homogeneous cargo except where this is clearly inappropriate, for example in the case of cargo spaces in a ship which are intended to be used exclusively for the carriage of vehicles or of containers.
(d)   Service loaded conditions, both (i) on departure and (ii) on arrival.
(2)(a)   A profile diagram of the ship drawn to a suitable small scale showing the disposition of all components of the deadweight.

(b)   A statement showing the lightweight, the disposition and the total weights of all components of the deadweight, the displacement, the corresponding positions of the centre of gravity, the metacentre and also the metacentric height (GM).

(c)   A diagram showing a curve of Righting Levers (GZ) derived from the cross curves of stability referred to in paragraph 9. Where credit is shown for the buoyancy of a timber deck cargo the curve of Righting Levers (GZ) must be drawn both with and without this credit.

(3)   The metacentric height and the curve of Righting Levers (GZ) shall be corrected for liquid free surface.

(4)   Where there is a significant amount of trim in any of the conditions referred to in sub-paragraph (1) the metacentric height and the curve of Righting Levers (GZ) may be required to be determined from the trimmed waterline.

(5)   If in the opinion of the Board the stability characteristics in either or both of the conditions referred to in sub-paragraph (1)(c) are not satisfactory, such conditions shall be marked accordingly and an appropriate warning to the master shall be inserted.

11.   Where special procedures such as partly filling or completely filling particular spaces designated for cargo, fuel, fresh water or other purposes are necessary to maintain adequate stability, a statement of instructions as to the appropriate procedure in each case.

12.   A copy of the report on the inclining test and of the calculation therefrom of the light condition particulars.

The information on hydrostatic particulars mentioned in paragraph 7 could be presented in the form which is illustrated on Page 108.

The diagram, information and curve of statical stability reproduced on the opposite page show a typical way in which the information required by paragraph 10 above could be presented. This diagram will be seen to illustrate paragraph 10 (1) (d) (i) and a further series of diagrams would have to be supplied to illustrate the other conditions detailed in paragraph 10. The diagrams may be collated in booklet form or displayed in the form of a chart under glass on a bulkhead or a desk top.

A displacement scale in "NOTES ON CARGO WORK" shows how the information required in paragraph 6 could be presented.

The Marine Division of the Department of Trade and Industry publish a Stability Information Booklet which indicates a recommended method of presenting the stability information to comply with The Merchant Shipping (Load Line) Rules 1968.

SERVICE LOADED (i) departure

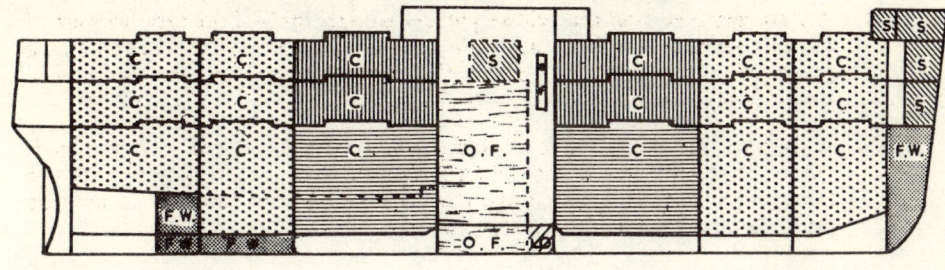

		Weight	Disposition	Kg
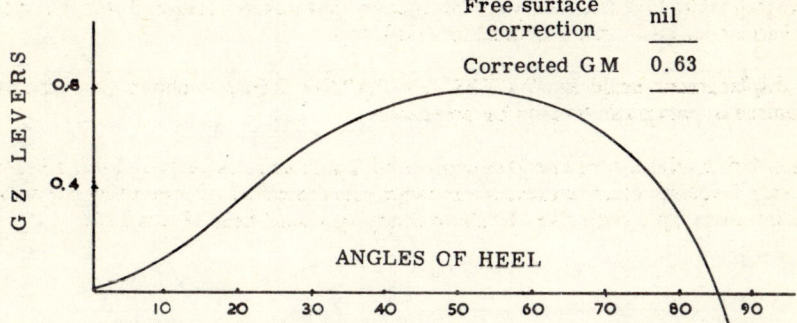 C	General cargo	(1525	U.T.D.	12.0
		(1960	L.T.D.	9.0
		(3500	L. Hold	6.1
C	Frozen meat	1020	L. Hold	6.1
C	Chilled meat (hung)	250	U.T.D.	12.8
		265	L.T.D.	10.4
O.F.	Oil Fuel	(400	Side Bunkers	6.3
		(500	D.B. Tanks	0.7
S	Stores & Provisions	40		13.5
F.W.	Fresh Water	(90	F.P. Tank	7.3
		(182	Deep Tank	3.3
		(66	D.B. Tanks	0.7
W.B.	Water Ballast	----		
L.O.	Lubricating oil & Engineers' Spares	90		10.0
	Passengers, Crew & Effects	10		16.0
	Total Deadweight	9898		
	Light Displacement	4570		7.5
	Load Displacement	14468		7.57

KM	8.2
Uncorrected GM	0.63
Free surface correction	nil
Corrected GM	0.63

GZ LEVERS

ANGLES OF HEEL

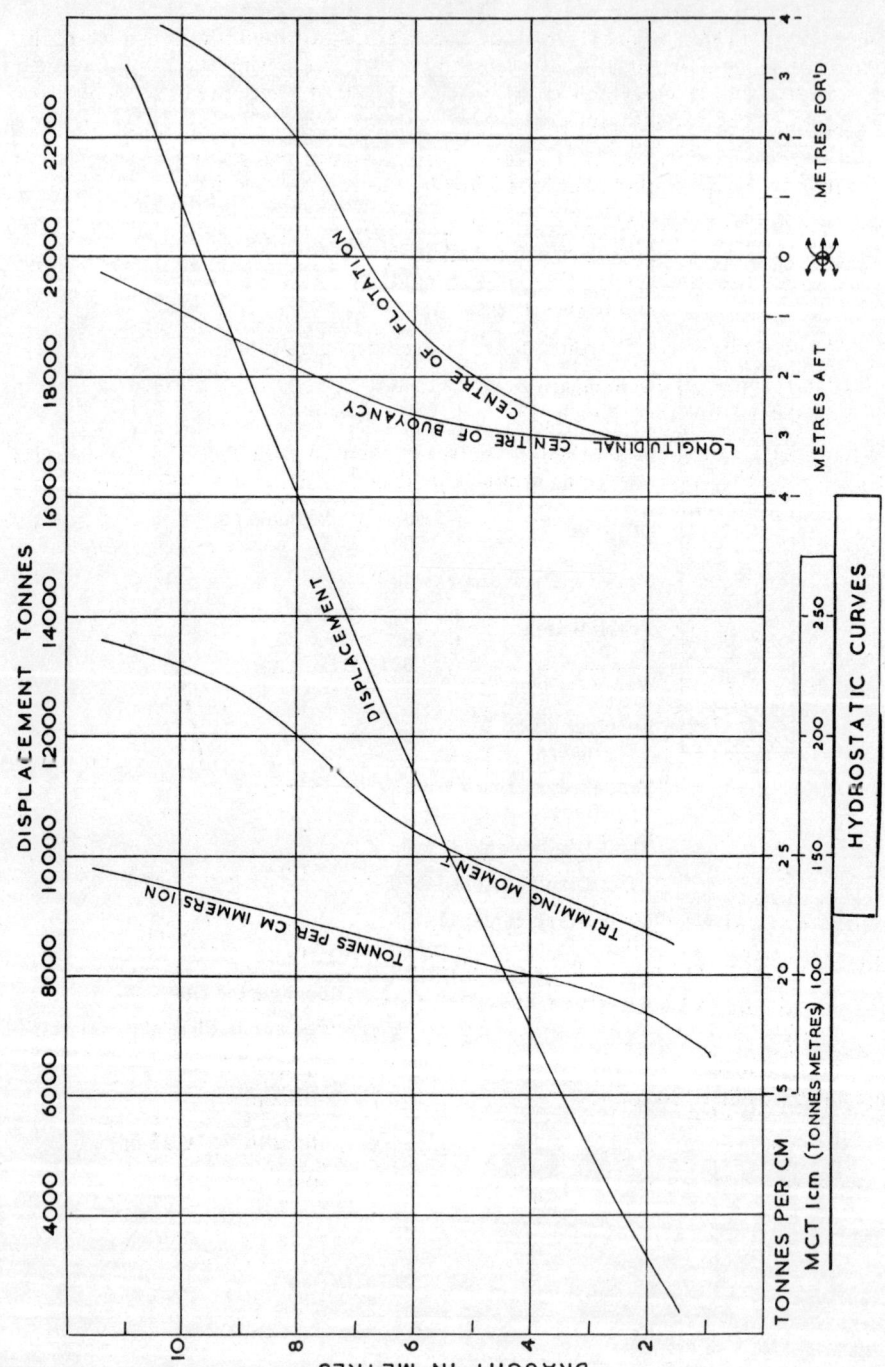

WORKED EXAMPLE 48
A vessel of length 156m whose hydrostatic curves are shown opposite is at present displacing 16000 tonnes. Her longitudinal centre of gravity is known to be 3.0 metres abaft midlength. Estimate her draught after loading 500 tonnes of cargo into No.4. hold whose centre of gravity is 28m abaft midlength.

From the curves at a displacement of 16000 tonnes the mean draught is 8.00 m.
Then, as all information is plotted against draught,

C.F.	2.00 m forward of midlength
L.C.B.	1.85 m abaft of midlength
TPC	22.3
MCT 1 cm	200 tonnes-metres

NOTE: The above information would be for an even keel condition

  If L.C.G. is 3.0m abaft midlength
  and L.C.B. is 1.85 m abaft midlength

i.e. a distance of 1.15 m between them if the vessel is on an even keel which constitutes a lever. To bring the vessel into longitudinal equilibrium a moment of 16000 x 1.15 m is required.

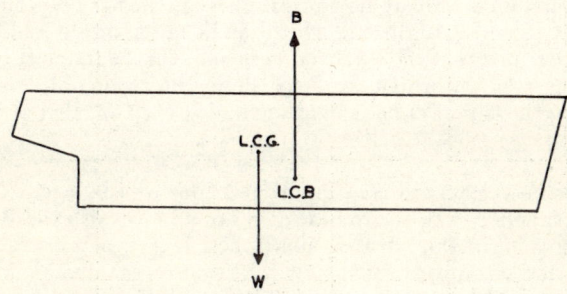

This causes a trim of $\dfrac{16000 \times 1.15}{200}$ by the stern $\qquad = \qquad$ 92cm

Trim due to loading 500 tonnes 30 m abaft C.F. $= \dfrac{500 \times 30}{200} \quad = \quad$ 75 cm

total trim   167 cm

Original mean draught	8.00 m	
Sinkage due to loading 500 tonnes	0.22 m	
New mean draught	8.22 m	8.22 m
Decrease forward due to trim $\dfrac{(76 \times 167)}{(156)}$	0.81 m	
Increase aft due to trim $\dfrac{(80 \times 167)}{(156)}$		0.86 m
Final draught	7.41 m F	9.08 m A

COMPUTATION OF STABILITY CONDITIONS FROM BASIC DATA

The text and examples on the foregoing pages have shown how to calculate GM, trim, draught, free surface effect and bending moments for a light or loaded ship. In each case the position of loading/discharging the weight (which must also be known accurately) is essential to the obtaining of a correct result which depends finally on accuracy of computation. This last stage is particularly tedious for many of the calculations, especially in practice with time at a premium, and can be done most accurately by mechanical or electronic means.

The "Ralston" stability and trim indicator is one of the best known of the 'automatic' calculators, and the description and illustration of it which follow have been kindly supplied by its makers Kelvin Hughes, and reprinted here with their permission.

The 'Ralston' Indicator is a simple instrument for weighing and balancing a ship under any and in every condition of loading and discharging. It is not a new instrument; a large number have been used by shipping lines throughout the world for many years. The 'Ralston' can be used by every class of ship and type of cargo, each indicator being custom built for the ship to which it is supplied.

It consists of a duralumin plate upon which is photo-etched the capacity or profile of the ship. This plate is attached to a frame which can be raised or lowered by means of levers resting on knife edge pivots at the sides and each end. On the frame at one end and at one side, scales are engraved, on which are fitted sliding blocks in order to balance the table. The block at the end of the frame is used in finding the GM; that at the side in finding trim.

Brass and duralumin weights representing from 2 tons to 1,000 tons (metric or imperial as required) are supplied with the indicator in accordance with the size and number of cargo compartments in the ship. In addition to these loose plates a series of special hinged weights, termed slacker flaps, are permanently fitted to the duralumin plate. Their purpose is to ascertain the loss of GM arising from free liquid surfaces due to the partial consumption, or transfer, of oil or water from the double bottoms or other tanks during the voyage.

The lid accommodates adjustable GM and Trim slides and a deadweight scale.

The tray is mounted in a hardwood cabinet, fitted with a compartment for convenient stowage of weights. The indicator tray and frame are made of brass and duralumin ensuring that there is no possibility of warp or distortion and it does not affect the compass if used in the wheelhouse.

The 'Ralston' weighs and balances the ship on the principle of a pair of scales. There is one small additional sum involved in using the 'Ralston'. Apart from this, the desired information is worked out visually by weights, slacker flaps and slides, with absolute accuracy.

When the tray is raised and balanced without weights and without slacker flaps turned down, the Light Weight condition of the ship is indicated, i.e. Light Draught, Trim and GM as derived by the builders from the Inclining Test.

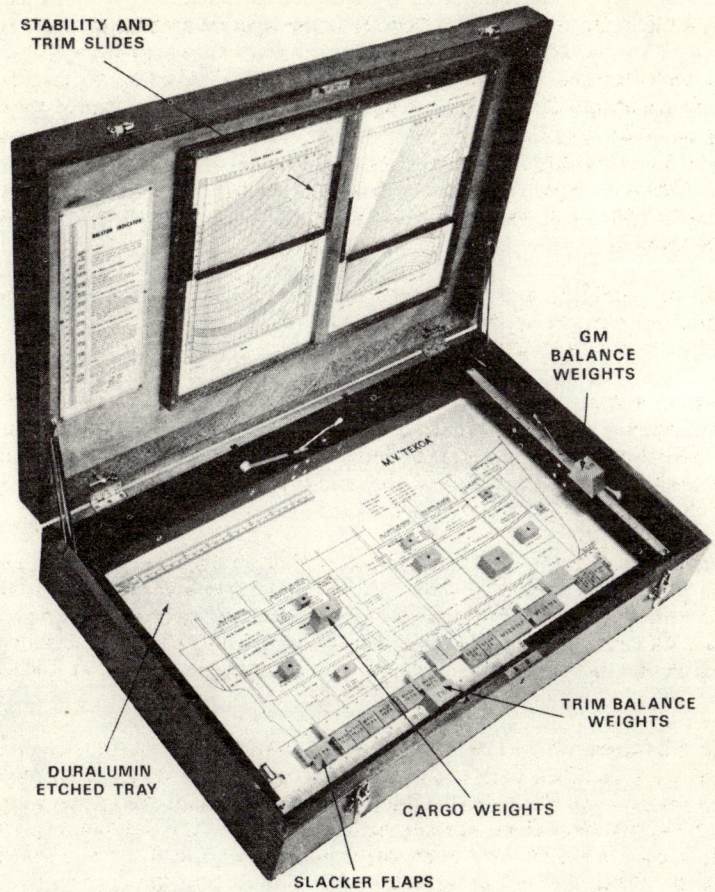

Allow **tray** to rest on the bottom of the box (not on pivots). Place weights to represent cargo, stores, water, passengers, etc., in positions on the tray corresponding to their actual positions on the ship. It is important that the weights are placed correctly, otherwise a true reading will not result.

In every compartment on the tray a small circle has been engraved to represent the Centre of Gravity of the whole compartment and is a useful guide when the space is full with a homogeneous commodity. If several weights are used in one compartment, place these one on top of the other at the estimated centre of gravity, add up all weights on the tray to arrive at the total deadweight.

Note the mean draught corresponding to this deadweight on the Deadweight scale in the lid of the box.

Raise tray by the end levers and balance it by moving the GM balancing weight along its rack until the built-in spirit level indicates that the tray is horizontal. Note the balance figure on the rack and adjust the GM slide in the lid accordingly. The GM can be seen where the curve cuts the Mean Draught.

Lower the end levers and raise tray by side levers. Balance this by adjusting the Trim balancing weight, as for GM. Note the balance figure on the trim rack and adjust the Trim slide in the lid accordingly. The Trim can be seen where the curve cuts the Mean Draught.

The above procedure is that which is required to test any existing cargo or for any proposed loading or discharge. If a negative or too small GM or a bad Trim is indicated, either reduce or alter cargo weights or add ballast tank weights until a satisfactory loading condition is obtained. Whenever weights are added or removed from the tray during such correction, it will be necessary to recalculate the new deadweight prior to reading off the GM and Trim figures.

The simple stress and bending moment calculations shown in chapter three become enormously complicated in practice and many hours of work would be required to complete a calculation. Fortunately, the calculations can be carried out on either mechanical or electronic computors and an example of each type is illustrated. Certain vessels are now required by classification societies to be supplied with means for calculating stresses whilst loading and each of the stress finders illustrated complies with the requirements of Lloyd's Register of Shipping. The fullest details of their use is supplied with the instruments which, as with any instrument depending on a ship's data, are custom calibrated for each ship.

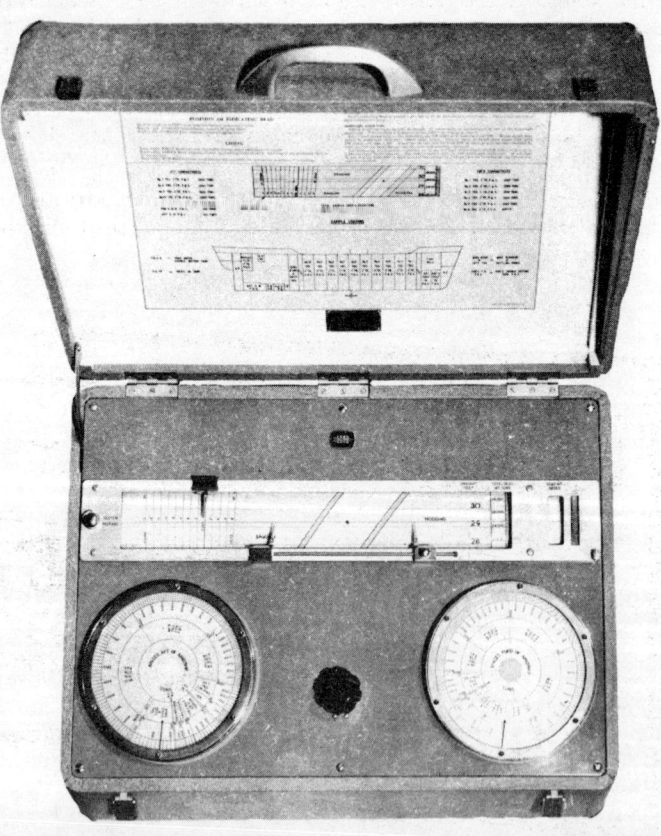

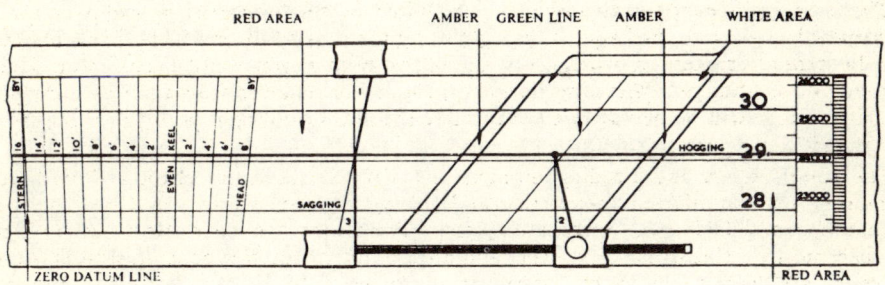

The illustration above of the Kelvin Hughes mechanical stress finder is supplied by the makers and reproduced with their kind permission. Portable, simple to operate and requiring no servicing it consists basically of two dials on which loadings forward and aft are set. The results are read by noting the position of a bead on a clear scale shown above the dials. The scale is coloured red, amber, white and green to indicate danger, marginal safe and optimum bead positions for bending moments. A further scale to the left enables trim to be indicated for the loading condition.

The GEC-Elliott electronic stress calculator, illustrated and described below by kind permission of the manufacturers, is one example of a number of electronic calculators which are now offered.

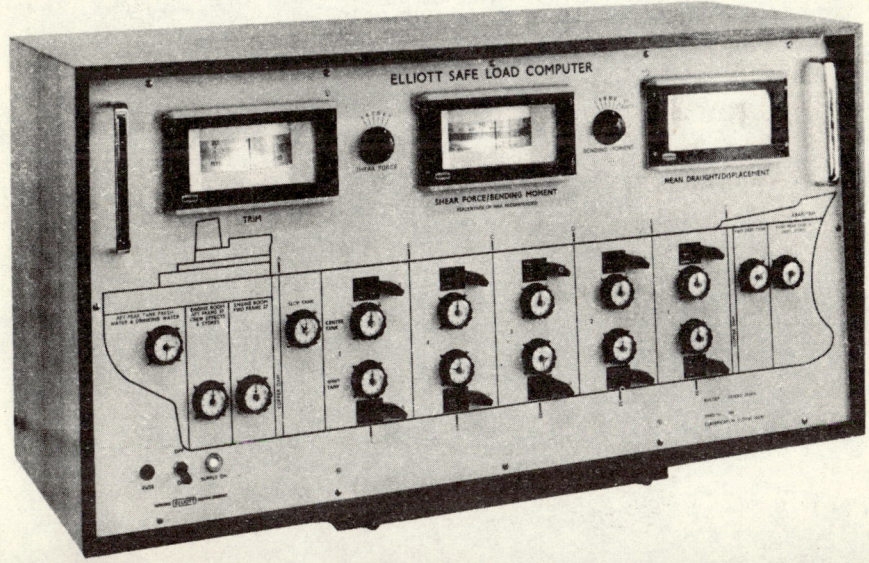

The calculator is a mathematical model of the vessel with dials representing the loadings in the tanks, holds or other compartments. A graphic diagram shows the distribution of the compartments throughout the vessel and the positions where readouts are given.

Because peak shear forces and bending moments never occur at the same place at the same time, the calculator provides readout points at carefully chosen positions where the peaks are most likely to occur.

Three indicators show continuously the trim, mean draught and displacement and the percentage of the maximum shear force or bending moment as recommended by the classification society.

Once the operator knows the nature and size of the cargo, he simply uses the loading dials to distribute the load in the calculator. Readings for trim and displacement are indicated simultaneously, enabling him to make any loading adjustments.

By using the switches provided he can scan the resultant shear forces and bending moments, see what points are unsafe and re-distribute the cargo accordingly.

All readings are continuously updated as loading data is applied, so that the officer can see immediately the overall effect of any alterations in the loading pattern. It is a quick and simple matter for him to continue re-distributing the load until the optimum results are obtained and the ship is correctly loaded for safe and profitable carrying.

The calculator fully meets the requirements of Lloyd's Register of Shipping and other classification societies for a safe load calculator which obtains results within ± 5% of their own results for the same loading conditions.

Tests of the above calculator have shown a calculation accuracy of ± 2% for Shear Force and ± 3% for Bending Moment. Trim can be read within ± 1 inch or 25 mm whilst draught can be resolved to ± ½ inch or 12 mm.

The calculator requires a mains A.C. single phase supply of either 110 or 230 volts 40-60 Hz. The power consumption is approximately 50-75 watts.

CHAPTER TEN

Use of Imperial Units

The theory of stability is exactly the same whether SI or Imperial Units are used and in any of the foregoing questions imperial units may be substituted for SI units if the reader requires exercises using imperial units. However although the theory is exactly the same there are differences between SI and Imperial formula for TPI, FWA and MCT $1''$ and the derivation of these follow the definition of the Imperial Units.

Length   expressed in either feet or inches

Weight   or force units expressed in tons

Density   Mass per unit volume expressed as ozs/cu.ft.

Moments   Force x distance usually foot-tons.

Pressure   Force per unit area either tons/square foot, or lbs/sq.ft.

DISPLACEMENT

Volume of displacement in cubic feet   =   L x B x d x Cb

Where L   =   length in feet

B   =   breadth in feet

d   =   draught in feet

Cb   =   block coefficient

Displacement   =   Volume displaced x density of water

In salt water density   =   1025 ozs/cu.ft.

So displacement tons in SW $= \dfrac{L \times B \times d \times Cb \times 1025}{2240 \times 16}$

$\dfrac{1025}{2240 \times 16}$ is usually taken as $\dfrac{1}{35}$

So displacement in SW   = $\dfrac{\text{Volume of displacement in cubic feet}}{35}$ Tons.

TONS PER INCH IMMERSION (TPI) is the additional tonnage displaced when the draught is increased by one inch.

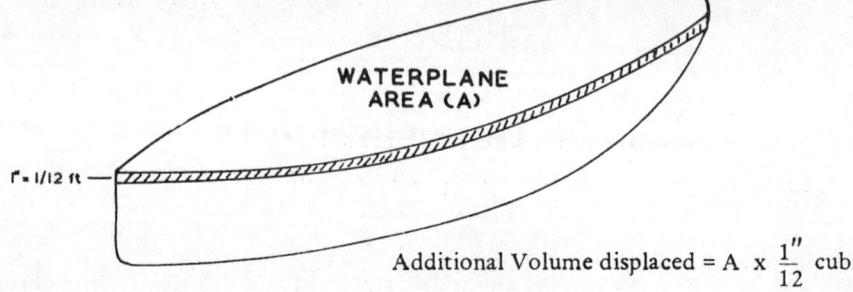

Additional Volume displaced = $A \times \dfrac{1''}{12}$ cubic feet.

$$\text{TPI} \quad = \quad \frac{A \times \delta \times 1''}{2240 \times 16 \times 12} \quad = \quad \frac{A \times 1025 \times 1''}{2240 \times 16 \times 12} \quad \text{(if } \delta \text{ is density of salt water)}$$

For practical purposes $\dfrac{1025}{2240 \times 16}$ is taken as being $\dfrac{1}{35}$, this makes T.P.I. $= \dfrac{A}{420}$

FRESH WATER ALLOWANCE (FWA)

When passing from salt water to fresh water, an additional volume is displaced, this will be $A (d_1 - d)$.

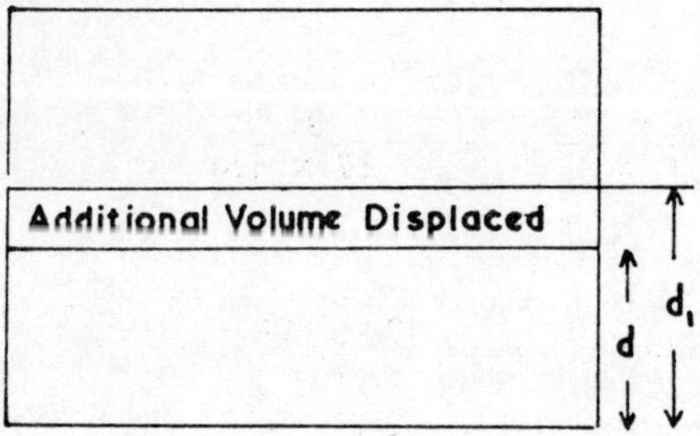

d is the draught in salt water

d_1 is the draught in fresh water

δ is the density of salt water namely 1025 ozs. per cu. ft.

δ_1 is the density of fresh water namely 1000 ozs. per cu. ft.

Also $\dfrac{V \times \delta}{2240 \times 16}$ $=$ displacement $= \dfrac{V \times \delta_1}{2240 \times 16} + \dfrac{A \times \delta_1 \times (d_1 - d)}{2240 \times 16}$

i.e. $V (\delta - \delta_1)$ $=$ $A \delta_1 (d_1 - d)$ $=$ $A \delta_1 \times$ FWA in feet

$V (1025 - 1000)$ $=$ $A \times 1000 \times$ FWA

$\dfrac{V \times 25}{1000}$ $=$ $A \times$ FWA   Now A $= \dfrac{2240 \times 16 \times 12 \times \text{TPI}}{1025}$

So FWA $= \dfrac{V \times 1025}{40 \times 2240 \times 16 \times 12 \times \text{TPI}}$

$= \dfrac{W \times 2240 \times 16 \times 1025}{1025 \times 40 \times 2240 \times 16 \times 12 \times \text{TPI}}$

$= \dfrac{W}{40 \times 12 \times \text{TPI}}$

FWA in inches $= \dfrac{12 \times W}{40 \times 12 \times \text{TPI}} = \dfrac{W}{40 \text{ TPI}}$

TO FIND THE MOMENT TO CHANGE TRIM ONE INCH (MCT 1$''$)

$$\frac{\text{Change of trim}}{\text{Length}} = \frac{GG_1}{GM_L} \quad \text{(please refer to diagram on page 69)}$$

$$\text{i.e. } GG_1 = \frac{GM_L \times \text{Change of trim}}{\text{Length of the vessel}}$$

The moment required to cause GG_1 is $W \times GG_1$

$$\text{So } W \times GG_1 = \frac{W \times GM_L \times \text{Change of trim}}{\text{Length of the vessel}}$$

If it is required to change the trim 1$''$, then $W \times GG_1$ is the MCT 1$''$.

$$\text{Then MCT 1}'' = \frac{W \times GM_L \times 1''}{L \text{ (in feet)}}$$

$$\text{Or MCT 1}'' = \frac{W \times GM_L}{12L} \quad \text{(note the 12 converts feet to inches)}$$

There are various approximations for MCT 1$''$., but they should only be used if there is insufficient information to enable one to use the above formula.

In a boxshape BM_L is nearly equal to GM_L.

$$BM_L = \frac{L^2}{12d}$$

$$\text{Then MCT 1}'' = \frac{L \times B \times d \times L^2}{35 \times 12 \times L \times 12d} = \frac{BL^2}{12 \times 420}$$

$$\text{But TPI} = \frac{A}{420} = \frac{L \times B}{420}$$

$$\text{Substituting we get MCT 1}'' = \frac{L \times TPI}{12} \quad \text{but } L = \frac{420 \times TPI}{B}$$

$$\text{so MCT 1}'' = \frac{420 \, (TPI)^2}{12B} = \frac{35 \, T^2}{B} \text{ (approx.)}$$

For a shipshape

$$\text{MCT 1}'' = \frac{30 \, T^2}{B} \text{ (approximately)}$$

$$\text{The change of trim in inches} = \frac{\text{Moments caused about the centre of flotation (foot tons)}}{\text{MCT 1}'' \text{ (foot tons)}}$$

When loading or discharging a weight,

The moment caused = The weight loaded or discharged x its distance from the centre of flotation.

When shifting a weight

The moment caused = The weight shifted x the distance it is shifted

Whilst it is again emphasised that it is as easy to work in SI units as in Imperial, and vice-versa, some readers may care to see some of the types of problems in imperial units and a few examples follow.

WORKED EXAMPLE 49 (Imperial units)

A vessel 450 feet in length, 60 feet in breadth and 40 feet in depth has a block coefficient of 0.833 and a waterplane coefficient of 0.77 at her summer load displacement of 18000 tons.

Calculate   (a)   her load draught

            (b)   her TPI at this draught

            (c)   her FWA

(a) $\text{Displacement} = \dfrac{\text{Volume of displacement}}{35} = \dfrac{L \times B \times d \times Cb}{35}$

Substituting and transposing we get

$$d = \frac{18000 \times 35}{450 \times 60 \times 0.833} = 28 \text{ feet}$$

(b) $\text{TPI} = \dfrac{A}{420} = \dfrac{450 \times 60 \times 0.77}{420} = 49.5$

(c) $\text{FWA} = \dfrac{W}{40\,\text{TPI}} = \dfrac{18000}{40 \times 49.5} = 9.09''$

WORKED EXAMPLE 50 (Imperial units)

A vessel of 8000 tons displacement KM 22.8 feet, assumed constant, KG 20.1 feet, loads the following:-

	600 tons KG	8 feet
	900 tons KG	30 feet
	500 tons KG	18 feet
she discharges	350 tons KG	4 feet
	150 tons KG	20 feet

What would be her moment of statical stability if heeled $6°$?

Taking moments about the keel

Weight	x	KG	=	Moment
8000		20.1		160800
600		8		4800
900		30		27000
500		18		9000
10000 tons				201600 foot-tons
- 350		4		- 1400
- 150		20		- 3000

Sum of the weights   9500 tons   Sum of the Moments   197200 foot-tons

New KG $= \dfrac{\text{Sum of moments}}{\text{Sum of weights}} = \dfrac{197200}{9500}$

$= 20.758$ feet

KM   22.800 feet

GM   2.042 feet

Moment of statical stability $= W \times GZ = W \times GM \sin \theta$

$= 9500 \times 2.042 \times \sin 6°$

$= 2027.7$ foot-tons

WORKED EXAMPLE 51 (Imperial units)

A vessel of 9500 tons displacement KM 24.5 feet, KG 23.0 feet, loads 500 tons Kg 20 feet and 4 feet to port of the centre line. Calculate her list.

$$\text{Vertical GG}_1 \quad = \quad \frac{w \times d}{W + w} \quad = \quad \frac{500 \times 3}{9500 + 500} \quad = \quad 0.15 \text{ feet down}$$

KG	23.0 feet	Old KG	23.00 feet
Kg	20.0 feet	new KG	22.85 feet
d	3.0 feet	KM	24.50 feet
		GM	1.65 feet

$$\text{Horizontal GG}_1 \quad = \quad \frac{w \times d}{W + w} \quad = \quad \frac{500 \times 4}{9500 + 500} \quad = \quad 0.2 \text{ feet}$$

$$\text{Tan } \theta \quad = \quad \frac{GG_1}{GM} \quad = \quad \frac{0.2}{1.65}$$

$$\theta \quad = \quad 6°55' \text{ to port.}$$

WORKED EXAMPLE 52 (Imperial units)

A vessel 450 feet in length, 60 feet breadth. TPI 49 is drawing $21' 04''$ F. $22' 08''$ A. and loads the following:-

230 tons in No.1.	170 feet forward of the centre of flotation
800 ” ” ” 3.	64 ” ” ” ” ” ” ”
500 ” ” ” 4.	67 feet abaft ” ” ” ” ”

She discharges 200 tons from No.2.   120 feet forward of the centre of flotation
105 tons from F.P.   200 feet   ”   ”   ”   ”   ”   ”

The centre of flotation is 15 feet abaft midlength. Calculate the new draught.

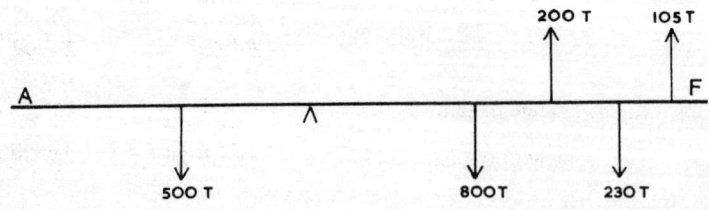

$$\text{MCT } 1'' = \frac{30 \, T^2}{B} = \frac{30 \times 49 \times 49}{60} = 1200.5 \text{ foot-tons}$$

Weight	x	Distance from centre of flotation	=	Moment	
				Forward	Aft
230		170 F		39100	-
800		64 F		51200	-
500		67 A		-	33500
- 200		120 F		-	24000
- 105		200 F		-	21000

net
weight   1225 tons
loaded

Forward: 90300 / 78500   Aft: 78500

Resultant moment 11800 foot-tons forward

$$\text{Sinkage} = \frac{\text{Weight loaded}}{\text{TPI}} \qquad\qquad \text{Change of trim} = \frac{\text{Resultant moment}}{\text{MCT } 1''}$$

$$= \frac{1225}{49} \qquad\qquad\qquad\qquad\qquad = \frac{11800}{1200.5}$$

$$= 25'' \qquad\qquad\qquad\qquad\qquad = 9.83'' \text{ by the head}$$

$$\text{Change of draught forward due to change of trim} = \frac{240}{450} \times 9.83'' = 5.24'' \text{ increase}$$

$$\text{Change of draught aft due to change of trim} = \frac{210}{450} \times 9.83'' = 4.59'' \text{ decrease}$$

	F	A
Old draughts	21' 04"	22' 08"
Sinkage	2' 01"	2' 01"
	23' 05"	24' 09"
Change due to change of trim	+ 5.24"	− 4.59"
New draughts	23' 10.24"	24' 04.41"

WORKED EXAMPLE 53 (Imperial units)

A barge 60 feet long has for its cross-section a rectangle on a triangle. The top section 30 feet wide and 6 feet deep forms a tank which is longitudinally divided on the centre line. The lower section which is 30 feet wide at the top tapering regularly through 7.5 feet to a point at the bottom also forms a tank. The upper tanks contain salt water to a depth of 1 foot whilst the bottom tank contains fresh water to a depth of 5 feet. Calculate the effective GM if the present KG is 6 feet and the vessel is floating at a draught of 7.5 feet in salt water.

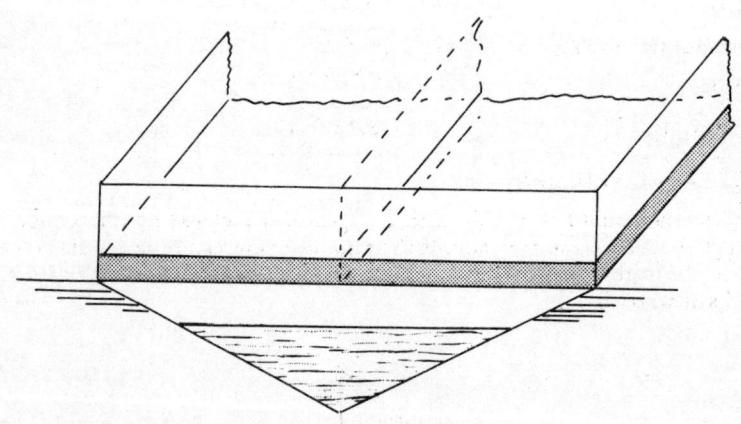

Volume of displacement $= L \times B \times \dfrac{d}{2} = 60 \times 30 \times \dfrac{7\,5}{2} = $ 6750 cu.ft.

Loss of GM due to free surface $= \dfrac{i}{V} \times \dfrac{\delta t}{\delta s} \times \dfrac{1}{n^2}$

$i = \dfrac{lb^3}{12}$ b for top tank is 30 feet

b for bottom tank is $\dfrac{5}{7.5} \times 30 = $ 20 feet

Loss for top tank $= \dfrac{60 \times 30 \times 30 \times 30}{12 \times 6750} \times \dfrac{1025}{1025} \times \dfrac{1}{4} = $ 5   feet

Loss for bottom tank $= \dfrac{60 \times 20 \times 20 \times 20}{12 \times 6750} \times \dfrac{1000}{1025} \times \dfrac{1}{1} = $ 5.78 feet

Total loss of GM due to free surface effect $= $ 10.78 feet

$$KM = KB + BM$$

$$= \frac{2}{3}d + \frac{B^2}{6d} \quad \text{as the underwater form is triangular}$$

$$BM = \frac{30 \times 30}{6 \times 7.5} = 20 \text{ feet}$$

$$KB = \frac{2}{3} \times 7.5 = 5 \text{ feet}$$

KM	25 feet
KG	6 feet
GM without free surface	19 feet
Loss of GM	10.78 feet
Effective GM	8.22 feet

WORKED EXAMPLE 54 (Imperial units)

A tank 60 feet long and 40 feet wide with a depth of 4 feet has its filling pipe 30 feet long at an angle of 45° to the tank top. If the tank overflows and the vessel is on an even keel, calculate the thrust on the tanktop. The cross sectional area of the filling pipe is 0.5 sq.ft. and salt water is used.

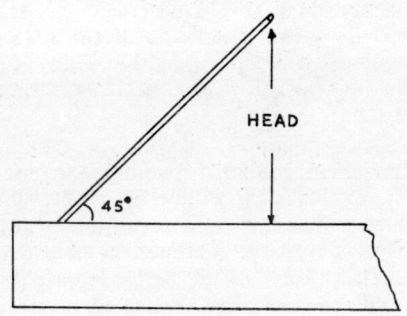

Height of water head above tanktop $=$ $30 \sin 45°$ $=$ 21.21 feet

$$\text{Thrust} = \frac{\text{Area under pressure} \times \text{pressure head}}{35} = \frac{60 \times 40 \times 21.21}{35}$$

$$= 1454.4 \text{ tons}$$

N.B. the area of the filling pipe is immaterial.

EXAMPLES FOR EXERCISE

1. A box-shaped vessel 100m in length 15m beam is floating at a draught of 5.3m in water relative density 1.013. Calculate the number of tonnes she can load, if her maximum permitted draught in salt water is 6.0m.

2. A vessel displacing 6800 tonnes is listed $5°$ to starboard with a GM of 0.7m. Calculate how many tonnes should be loaded in the port 'tween deck 4m to port of the centre line and 0.3m above the old C.G. in order to bring the vessel upright.

3. A vessel of 12500 tonnes KM 8.5m KG 7.0m is floating upright. She then loads the following:- 400t, KG 5m; 770t, KG 6.8m; 300t, KG 0.5m; 835t, KG 10m. She discharges 460t, KG 9m; 565t, KG 8m. Calculate her list if 100 tonnes of oil is transferred from port to starboard, a distance of 14 metres.

4. A vessel which displaces 14000 tonnes when floating at an even keel draught of 8.25 metres has a length on the waterplane of 144 metres. The semi-ordinates of her waterplane at equidistant intervals are, starting from forward:- 0, 2.7, 5.9, 8.3, 10.6, 10.6, 9.9, 6.4 and 2.1 metres respectively. Calculate the position of the centre of flotation, her fresh water allowance and her waterplane coefficient.

5. A double bottom tank 20m long 16m wide 1m depth has a centreline longitudinal watertight division. Calculate the vessel's list if the port side of this tank is half filled with oil relative density 0.975. Assume the vessel's displacement in salt water, KM and KG before loading the oil to have been 9422 tonnes, 8.4 and 7.5 metres respectively.

6. A ship of length 150m drawing 8.2m forward 9.35m aft with MCT 1cm of 210 tonnes-metres and TPC 25, loads the following:- 300t, 40m forward of C.F; 350t, 52m abaft C.F; 100t at C.F; 225t, 12m forward of C.F. A further quantity of cargo is expected, space is available in the after hold 63m abaft C.F. and in the forward 'tween decks. How much should be loaded aft if the draught aft is to be 10.0m and where should the remainder be stowed to maintain this after draught? The C.F. is 5m abaft midlength.

7. A vessel drawing 6.65m forward 7.33m aft is required to complete loading at a mean draught of 8.00m and be trimmed 0.5m by the stern. Space is available 43m forward of C.F. and 48m abaft C.F. How much cargo should be loaded in each position to achieve the required draught? MCT 1cm 175 tonnes-metres; TPC 18. C.F. amidships.

8. A vessel drawing 6.75m forward and 7.95m aft is to enter a channel with a maximum even keel draught of 7.4m. The forepeak tank 60m from the C.F. is the only empty tank and this may be filled, either from overside and/or by transferring water ballast from No.5 D.B. tank (capacity 120 tonnes) 40m abaft C.F. How much should be run into and/or transferred to the forepeak to obtain the correct trim at maximum draught? MCT 1cm 150 tonnes-metres; TPC 20.

9. A box-shaped vessel 125 metres in length 18 metres beam is floating at a draught of 9 metres with a KG of 7.0m. A discharge pipe amidships on the starboard water-line is fractured and in order to make repairs it is to be brought 1 metre above the water. How much oil should be shifted from side to side, a distance of 10 metres, to achieve this?

10. A ship is floating on an even keel in salt water at a draught of 7.5m. Her waterplane length, breadth and coefficient are 150m, 16m and 0.833 respectively. A double bottom tank 19m long 15m wide and 1.2m deep is to be filled by opening the sea valve and allowing the water to run in. Calculate the maximum thrust on the tank top.

11. A vessel of 9300 tonnes, KM 9.25 metres is inclined by shifting 15 tonnes horizon-tally across the deck 21 metres. It is noted that the mean deflection of a plumbline 13.5 metres long is 35.5 centimetres, calculate her KG.

12. The tonnes per centimetre immersion of a vessel up to her load draught of 15.2 metres are given for equally spaced waterlines as follows:-
                0, 18.5, 19.4, 20.4, 21.6, 23.3, 24.7, 26.0, 27.5.
    Calculate her displacement in salt water and the position of the centre of buoyancy checking the latter by Morrish's formula.

13. A vessel of length 186m drawing 9.45m forward and 10.35m aft loads 200t, 20m forward of the C.F. and 375t, 45m abaft the C.F. She then discharges 95t from a point 25m abaft the C.F. Calculate the new draughts if the C.F. is 5m abaft mid-length, the moment to change trim 1 cm is 270 tonnes-metres and the TPC is 32.

14. A box-shaped vessel 150 metres in length and 20 metres beam is floating at a draught of 7 metres in salt water with a KG of 7.6 metres. A midship compartment extending across the vessel and 25 metres long is bilged. Calculate her moment of statical stability if heeled $5°$.

15. A box-shaped vessel 150 metres long, 25 metres beam, is floating on an even keel in salt water at a draught of 6 metres. A midship compartment length 30 metres containing cargo stowing at 2.0 cubic metres per tonne, relative density 0.625, is bilged. Calculate the new draught.

16. A box-shaped vessel length 100m, beam 12m, depth 10m is floating at a draught of 6.0m in salt water. Her KG is 4.5m. What is:-
    a)   Her metacentric height?
    b)   The moment of statical stability when heeled $20°$?
    c)   The dynamical stability when heeled $20°$?

17. A vessel 216 metres in length has the following equally spaced ordinates on the bottom plating which is assumed to be flat. 0, 12, 16, 18.3, 19.6, 20, 18.1, 13.1, 6.9 and 1.9 metres. What is the upthrust on the bottom plating if the vessel is floating at a draught of 8 metres in water of relative density of 1.018?

18. A waterplane is defined by the following ordinates:-
    0, 2.4, 3.3, 3.4, 2.9 and 0.6 metres. If the vessel is 15 metres long calculate the TPC at her present draught.

19. A vessel is floating at a draught of 7.3m forward and 7.0m aft. Given TPC 20 and MCT 1cm 125 tonnes-metres, calculate how much cargo to load into No.4. hold c.g. 45m abaft the centre of flotation and No.1. hold 60m forward of the centre of flotation, to bring the vessel to an even keel at a draught of 7.5m. Centre of flotation is amidships.

20. A vessel of light displacement 3500 tonnes KG 6.5m KM 7.2m has to load 9000 tonnes of ore. KG of lower hold 6.0m and 'tween deck 13.0m. If the only requirement is to have a righting moment of 500 tonnes-metres at $8°$ when loaded, how much cargo should be loaded into each available position?

21. A ship 200m in length, displacement 12200 tonnes leaves port on an even keel. She consumes 600 tonnes of fuel KG 0.75m; 8m forward of the C.F. and 150 tonnes of water KG 6.0m; 96m forward of C.F. Calculate the quantity of water to transfer from the after peak (cap. 100t) to the fore peak a distance of 170m and what to load, if necessary, into a D.B. tank 40m forward of C.F. KG 0.8m to bring the vessel back to even keel.

22. A ship with draughts F 10.5m A 13.0m has to berth where there is only 13.0m of water alongside. Working on a minimum clearance of 0.2m under the keel, calculate the ballast to take 25m forward of the C.F. which is 2m abaft midlength. Length 180m, TPC 18, MCT 1cm 100.

23. A ship displacing 9980 tonnes GM 0.8m KG 11.0m lifts a container weighing 20 tonnes. Find the list when the container is first lifted off the jetty. The derrick is plumbed 16m outboard and the head block is 16m above the jetty and 21m above the keel. Find also the list when the container is placed aboard having a KG 9m and 9m outboard of C/L.

24. A beam 20m long of negligible weight is loaded with 20 tonnes evenly spread. Draw a shear force and bending moment curve and find the values of both 6m from one end, if the beam is supported on knife edges at each end.

25. A cantilever 10m long of negligible weight has a 5 tonne weight attached at the free end. Draw S.F. and B.M. curves and find shear and the bending moment at mid-length.

26. A vessel of length 120 metres, draught 6.2m forward and 7.0m aft has MCT 1cm 100 and TPC 12. Find the weight of water to pump out of the after peak so that she can pass over a bar with depth of water 6.9m with a clearance of 20 centimetres. The after peak is 50m aft of the CF which is 2m abaft mid-length.

27. The ½ ordinates of a vessel's waterplane are 0; 2.4; 5.4; 7.2; 7.8; 9.0; 9.6; 8.4; 7.2; 4.2; 0. If the waterplane is 140 m long find the TPC at this draught in fresh water and the position of the centre of flotation.

28. A box-shaped vessel length 20m breadth 9m depth 7m floating in freshwater on an even keel of 2.0m has a KG 4.0m, and loads 540 tonnes of concentrate spread evenly with a KG of 3.0m. Calculate the original GM and also the loaded GM.

29. A ship displacing 10000 tonnes has a GM 1.0m and is listed 4° to starboard. It is required to load a further 250 tonnes KG 10.0m. Assume KM of 12.0m is constant. Space is available 6.0m to starboard of centre line and 4.0m to port of centre line. How much cargo should be loaded into each if the vessel is to be upright on completion?

30. Estimate the amount of cargo aboard a vessel 150m in length, draught of 6.6m F 9.8m A, centre of flotation 2m abaft mid-length and stores and fuel 300 tonnes. The displacement curve gave the following information:-

Draught	Displacement in tonnes
8.4m	11090
8.0m	10570
2.5m (light)	3700

ANSWERS TO EXERCISES

1. 1171.65 tonnes (1187t if FWA is used)
2. 104.125 tonnes.
3. 3°33′
4. 80.41 m from forward. FWA 170.5 mm
    Cw 0.656
5. 2°09½′ to port
6. 101.2 tonnes; 18 m forward of C.F.
7. 993.5t forward; 824.5t aft.
8. Transfer 120 tonnes. Load 100 tonnes
9. 115.3 tonnes
10. 1890.34 tonnes
11. 7.962 metres
12. 32407.7 tonnes; 8.464 metres; 8.739 metres.
13. 9.395 m forward: 10.684 m aft
14. 1065.5 tonnes-metres
15. 6.25 metres

16. (a) 0.5 m (b) 1596.4 tonnes-metres
     (c) 250 tonnes-metres approximately.
17. 24737.4 tonnes
18. 0.395
19. 264.3 t in No. 1 435.7 t in No. 4.
20. 1379.62 t in T.D. 7620.38 t in L.H.
21. Transfer all A.P. and load 55 tonnes
22. 300 tonnes
23. 2°21′: 1°17′.
24. S.F. 4 tonnes +ve. B.M. 42 t-m +ve
25. S.F. 5 tonnes +ve. B.M. 25 t-m −ve.
26. 92.3 tonnes
27. 17.248; 74 metres from 1st ordinate
28. 0.375 m; 0.45 m
29. 219.93 tonnes to port; 30.07 tonnes to starboard.
30. 6885.5 tonnes

INDEX

Angle of Loll 52, 53, 100
Archimedes' Principle 4
Atwood's Formula 48

Bending Moment 28
Bilging 9, 81
Block Coefficient 6
BM 42, 43

Carriage of Stability Information 104
Centre of Area 19, 22
Centre of Buoyancy 5, 23, 24, 108
Centre of Flotation 68, 108
Centre of Gravity 6, 13, 57
Centre of Pressure 89
Change of Trim 68
Coefficient (Block) 6
Coefficient (Prismatic) 6
Coefficient (Waterplane) 6, 19
Conditions for Stable Equilibrium 51
Correction to Mean Draught 80
Couple 46
Cross Curves of Stability 101
Curves of Metacentres 45
Curve of Statical Stability 97, 102

Density 4, 115
Discharging Weights 54
Displacement 7, 108, 115
Draught (Change with Density) 7, 82, 108, 116
Draught when heeled 66
Draught (keeping constant) 75
Drydocking 84
Dynamical Stability 47, 48, 103

Effect of Free Surface 92
Examples for Exercise 124

Flooding 9, 81
Formulae 129, 130
Fresh Water Allowance 8, 116

GEC-Elliot Safe Load Computer 113

Hydrostatic Curves 108

Imperial Units 115
Inclining Test 63
Inertia (moment of) 41
Initial Stability 47

KN Curves 101

Lever 46
Loading Weights 54
Loll (angle of) 52
Longitudinal Metacentre 41, 69
Loss of GM due to dry docking 84, 86

Loss of GM due to free surface 93
Lost Buoyancy 9

M.C.T. 1" 117
M.C.T. 1 cm 69, 70, 108
Metacentre 41
Metacentric Curves 45
Metacentric Height 41
Metacentric Stability 46
Moment 4, 12, 115
Moment (Bending) 28
Moment of Statical Stability 46
Morrish's Formula 5
Moseley's Formula 48

Neutral Equilibrium 51

Period of Roll 65
Permeability 9
Pressure 4, 88
Prismatic Coefficient 6

Ralston Stability Indicator 110
Relative Positions of B, G & M 50
Reserve Buoyancy 5
Righting Lever 46
Righting Moment 46
Rolling 65

Shear 27
Shifting Weights 57
Shift of B 42, 82
Shift of G 54, 57, 93, 98
SI units 3
Simpson's Rules 15
Specific Gravity 4
Stability at large angles 47
Stable Equilibrium 50, 51
Statical Stability 46
Stress Indicator 112, 113
Suspended Weights 62
Synchronism 65

Thrust due to Liquid 88
Tipping Centre 68
Tons per Centimetre Immersion 7, 108
Tons per Inch Immersion 116
Transverse Metacentre 41
Trapezoidal Rule 15
Trim 68

Unstable Equilibrium 51
Unsymmetrical Loading 59
Upthrust due to dry docking 85

Wall Sided Formula 49
Waterplane Coefficient 6
Wave Period 65